# SENSATIONS & DISABILITY

Published in the U.K. by ROMPA
ISBN 0 9512821 1 5

General Rehabilitation/Therapy

Printed in Great Britain by Polestar Wheatons Ltd, Exeter

*1*

*With thanks to John Newton for taking a risk
and Cliff Cunningham for helping our confidence*

## COMMENTS FROM THE PUBLISHER - ROMPA

In 1992 we started to ask many people of different disciplines, who all had the common goal of caring for people, if they would commit to paper their experiences of working with SNOEZELEN.

Roger Hutchinson and Joe Kewin agreed to edit the papers. Their work and research into Sensory Environments made them an obvious choice and we appreciate their input.

We would also like to acknowledge the silent contribution of Ad Verheul and Jan Hulsegge whose original work on SNOEZELEN has been an inspiration to many individuals throughout the world.

Many of you will be aware that SNOEZELEN, outside Belgium, the Netherlands and Luxembourg, is a Registered Trade Mark of ROMPA. What this means to Professionals and Carers is that ROMPA will not withhold the use of the word by Caring Professionals. However, our decision to register the name was borne out of a quality issue in that we firmly believe that SNOEZELEN equipment and training should be both appropriate and of high quality. We will therefore not licence the use of the name to organisations who cannot or will not meet high standards of safety and ethical practice.

**STUART BRITLAND for ROMPA**

Spring 1994.
*Both ROMPA and SNOEZELEN are Registered Trade Marks.*

# Foreword

This collection of writings should not be approached as if they are in some way a 'seminal' work in the area of Snoezelen. Rather they have been collected together to provide the reader with an introduction to the way in which Sensory activity and Snoezelen in particular has been applied in the field of severe disability. Some of the text is descriptive, some outlines the outcome of research activity and some considers ideas for future applications. All the authors use sensory activity with their respective service users as a means of enhancing communication, developing and sharing experiences and improving the relationship between the person and their surrounding environment. By designing environments that provide positive, pleasurable experiences and developing relationships with 'carers' in which these experiences can be shared, it is possible to enable people with a severe or profound multiple disability to gain access to a world that is meaningful and liberating rather than restrictive and confusing. Enlightened service providers purposely design specialised facilities for people with a physical disability whilst at the same time limiting the disablement resulting from a disability by ensuring that 'ordinary' experiences are accessible to the person with a physical, visual or auditory impairment. The ideas outlined in the text clearly demonstrate that this approach is also possible when considering people with severe or profound multiple disability. With sensitivity and creativity it is possible to enable people with the most severe and profound disability to enjoy experiences that are meaningful to them. Care must be taken to ensure that relationships developed and experiences enjoyed are sensitive to the ethnic environment which the person occupies. Hence ideas outlined should be adapted to the individuals cultural and religious circumstances. In a similar way the ideas can be adapted to any environment which is occupied by a person with a temporary disability as a result of which the person need stimulation of the primary senses to aid rehabilitation - an intensive care unit; a hospice; following head injury etc. Music, lighting, smells and massage also have their place in helping to reduce stress and promote relaxation in fields as diverse as maternity services, services for people who are elderly and confused and services for people who suffer chronic pain. The ideas outlined can be applied in a wide variety of settings, the only limitation being set by the creativity of the reader.

Roger Hutchinson
Joe Kewin

# CONTENT

**Title of Chapter**                                         **Page no**

Snoezelen - The Reason and the Method      *J. Kewin*              6

The Development and Evaluation of a Snoezelen Leisure Resource
for People with Severe Multiple Disability
*R. Hutchinson   L. Haggar*                                      18

A short training package for care staff using Snoezelen
environments with Profoundly and Multiply Disabled Clients:
Design, Implementation and Evaluation      *L. Haggar*          49

People with a Disability - Therapists and Sensory Activity
*A. Moore   G. Harris   J. Stephens*                           88

Sensory Environments - A Management  Perspective
*J. Kewin*                                                     120

Snoezelen in Education      *M. Gallaher   M. Balson*          129

A Study in the use and implication of the Snoezelen Resources
at Limington House School        *A. Bunsen*                  138

Balders Hus (The House of Balder) the old house with the new ideas
*M. Melberg   G.Jansson*                                      163

Snoezelen - an Evaluation of a sensory environment used by people
who are elderly and confused      *L. Pinkney   P. Barker*    172

Snoezelen - Experiences from a day hospital for adults with mental
health difficulties      *K. Smith   P. McAllister*           184

Sensory Environments and Experiences - Some ideas for their
application      *R. Hutchinson*                              196

The role of Sensation in the management of Chronic Pain
*P. Scholfield*                                               213

Sensory Activity - a Summary   *R. Hutchinson   J. Kewin*     229

# SNOEZELEN - THE REASONS AND THE METHOD

**Joe Kewin**

Many of us who have cared for, and worked with, people who have profound sensory, physical and learning disabilities will recognise the frustrations involved in trying to provide them with appropriate, interesting and stimulating experiences. Carers, teachers and therapists are often faced with the same questions. How do we find age appropriate, ability appropriate and culturally acceptable things that will help the person to gain some immediate or lasting benefit? How can we find an appropriate activity when so little attention has been paid to the needs of some of the most disabled members of society?

How many of us have opened the equipment of the games cupboard on a Monday morning and looked in despair at the array of posting boxes, shapes, puzzles, tactile dominoes and finger paints hoping for inspiration? It is when we consider that there are five mornings and afternoons ahead of us that the despair can dampen the enthusiasm of even the most creative staff member. What we are often seeking is something to stimulate interest, encourage motivation or help us to develop a meaningful relationship with the person. It is perhaps courageous to accept that in most institutions the act of being washed and dressed, handled into a wheelchair and pushed to an activity classroom is as stimulating and beneficial to the individual as the resulting activity itself. To experience the physical contact of others, the demands of movements, changes in temperature, bumps from uneven surfaces, the wind and the rain, will help us to realise that we are alive and sharing our environment with other people.

Whilst the essential work of the teacher and the therapist will continue in their search for mobility and development, it is the realisation that we have a need and a right to receive a wide range of stimulation and experiences that has led some to explore new opportunities.

At Whittington Hall in Chesterfield, we were involved in changing our activity base from a craft orientation to one of sensory experience as a direct response to the changing needs of our residents and our own awareness that those who remained had a right to experience positive feelings of pleasure and relaxation. Whilst the concept of providing sensory experiences to reduce tension and produce pleasure is not new, it is often difficult for staff who have traditionally helped people to make things or develop domestic skills to accept the value involved in very basic sensory experiences. We frequently stand away from our residents, touching them for direct care purposes only.

Whilst there are many exceptions to this statement, the fact remains that many people who live in institutions receive very little positive contact with others. They may have to draw attention to themselves by developing threatening or demanding behaviour. Those who are less mobile and present little threat may spend long periods facing the same spot in a room or looking at the ceiling because they are unable to move themselves to change their position.

Developments in sensory integration theory and activity provided us with a suitable justification to embark on a spree of sensory experience exploration. The idea that it was "therapeutic" to activate the brain by stimulating the primary senses gave us a culturally acceptable way (as Health workers) of rationalising our desire to invent new pastimes.

We used coloured lights, essential oils, fans, massage, textures, sounds and smells to create experiences. The inhibitions of the staff slowly gave way as we recognised the pleasure in the response of our residents to the new atmosphere. This developed into an Aladdin's cave of sensory experience where people appeared to relax free from the pressure to achieve tasks or the need to fight for attention.

On hearing of the Dutch experience with Snoezelen, we were quick to adopt their concept of developing a variety of permanent rooms to provide sensory experience. It is perhaps a little wonder that most carers, teachers and therapists see the value in providing basic sensory stimulation. What prevents us from putting our ideas into practice is the limitation of our budget or the traditional values that require us to provide "classroom activities". We overcame these problems by adopting the concept of leisure. Our Snoezelen Centre is in effect a leisure centre where the user has a choice of a wide variety of experiences. The approach adopted is an "enabling" one where we are sensitive to the need of the individual and where we accept the need for contact and sharing. In applying this concept, we also fulfil some essential "quality of care" requirements providing the best possible quality of life for those in our care as we expand the experiences open to them.

The result of our experience has been to see major benefit in relationships. We can truly say that we are now more accepting of people as interesting individuals in their own right. We now have a means of allowing people to express themselves in an environment free from pressure where attitudes and equipment enable choices and involvement. Staff are more relaxed, feeling that they are making a major contribution to the lives of those in their care. We all enjoy pleasant surroundings, and a choice of things to do that we can do. Whilst this is easy to say, it is difficult to provide for people who have profound disabilities.

After the initial release of ideas and the adoption of the Snoezelen concept, we have seen the further development of Snoezelen rooms in residential bungalows and hostels for the profoundly disabled. A team leader in one of these residential homes describes the Snoezelen room as "our colour television. Instead of watching the shapes and colours, and listening to the sounds of the television, we can step inside this room and experience the sensations first hand".

Snoezelen has given us the means to provide a wide range of sensory experiences that increase the quality of life of the individual. It also allows us to provide meaningful activity without the need for intellectual or development pursuits. Whilst these often follow naturally, the major benefit appears to be the release of stress and frustration. Through the adoption of the Snoezelen concept, we have the means to share pleasurable experiences. So often it is difficult for us to tell people that we care, but with Snoezelen we can show them that we do.

## SNOEZELEN - Questions and Answers

Snoezelen consists of pleasurably sensory experiences generated in an atmosphere of trust and relaxation. The sensory experiences are arranged to stimulate the primary senses without the need for intellectual activity. Trust and relaxation are encouraged by a non-directive or enabling approach being adopted by the helper or carer.

### Where did Snoezelen come from?

Snoezelen was developed in Holland with the intention of providing people who have sensory and learning disabilities with appropriate relaxation and leisure facilities. It originates from the belief that we all need stimulation. People who have special needs also have the right to appropriate stimulation. This may require the development of special environments to enable the participation of the person.

### What type of developments are there?

These range from small and large rooms to major centres. Individual items of equipment can help to create an atmosphere and provide stimulation whilst a fully developed Snoezelen environment will have additional benefits. Rooms have been developed in homes, hostels, schools, hospitals, ATCs and leisure centres.

### Is Snoezelen a therapy?

Whilst the approach taken in Snoezelen is non-directive, it is recognised that Snoezelen can be of great therapeutic value in providing opportunities for exploration and development.

The essence of the Snoezelen approach is to allow the individual the time, space and opportunity to enjoy the environment at their own pace, free from the expectations of others.

## What are the benefits?

Above all, Snoezelen provides an environment for relaxation through gentle stimulation. In many cases, this will involve contact with others in a caring atmosphere. Communication and understanding between participants can be improved as the pressure to achieve is removed and the trust develops. People who have perceptual difficulties appear to gain pleasure from the visual, auditory and tactile experiences. Carers can share the experience whilst often seeing people in a new light (Whittington Hall research).

## Who can benefit from Snoezelen?

Originally developed as a leisure experience for people who had severe learning difficulties and sensory disabilities, it is now used on a much wider scale. It has been of major benefit for people who are very active or who have self-injurious behaviour. People with sensory, physical and intellectual disabilities gain from the wide variety of stimulation as do those who have problems related to autism. For many of these people, it is not only the facilities but also the attitude adopted in them that is beneficial. Elderly confused people who have difficulty relating to existing environments or to demands made upon them also appear to benefit from the basic and primary sensory stimulation that Snoezelen offers. The gentle stimulation has a soothing effect that helps relieve agitation.

The carer (friend, staff or family) also enjoys the Snoezelen environment whilst gaining new insights. The need for the carer to produce something or to encourage and direct development is removed, allowing them the opportunity to relax.

## Why use Snoezelen?

We all have a need for stimulation and leisure. This is essential for relaxation and recuperation. Whilst elaborate facilities are designed and provided for the majority of people, there are very few facilities created for those people who have special perceptual needs. Snoezelen aims to cater for some of these needs. The enabling approach adopted by the carer is essential to the Snoezelen concept. This reduces the pressure to conform or perform and enables choice, an essential ingredient for leisure and relaxation.

Whilst other activities, therapies and teaching can continue, Snoezelen offers an additional opportunity for the individual and the carer to relax, explore and express themselves in an open atmosphere of trust and pleasure.

For many users, Snoezelen will provide the widest and most appropriate range of stimulation that they may have experienced. Used on a regular basis, this will broaden their experience and opportunity whilst enriching their contact with people and things.

## How do we create the Snoezelen environment?

The environment is of major importance. It must be inviting and comfortable whilst providing stimulation in an adaptable and acceptable way. Choice and control over aspects of the environment should be included where appropriate.

People will prefer different effects so it is necessary to be responsive to their needs and to develop adaptable facilities.

Individual pieces of equipment or combinations should be used to generate the desired atmosphere. Different rooms can provide a wider range of stimulation and participation.

White rooms are used to provide gentle stimulation and relaxation. The white walls and ceiling absorb the pastel colours projected onto them to create different experiences. The White room is the most popular environment providing the essential components for Snoezelen.

Rooms offering a greater degree of control to the participant can be developed using a range of switches and a wide variety of stimulating effects. Floors and walls can be made to change colour or vibrate when activated by switches that are responsive to pressure or sound. These rooms achieve their best effect when they can act as a library or stimulation offering a choice to the participant. The aim is to enable the participant the opportunity to control his environment and explore at his own pace.

Adventure rooms that incorporate soft fittings, obstacles, steps, ball pools, etc can also include the Snoezelen concept by the addition of appropriate lighting and sound equipment and the adoption of the enabling attitude. These rooms often provide valuable opportunities for more active people to express themselves whilst the variety of spaces, corners and enclosures can also allow an individual the chance to escape from the attention of others.

## Lighting

Projectors, spotlights, star panels, UV lights, mirror balls, bubble tubes and other lights will provide a variety of effects whilst helping to create warm and cool sensations. They can provide interest, pleasurable relaxation and stimulation. Gentle changes of light patterns and colours are relaxing and interesting. Powerful and sudden changes from dark to light are avoided in Snoezelen as these can be alarming and uncomfortable.

The Whittington Hall evaluation of Snoezelen did not record any adverse effects of the use of lighting for those people who have severe epilepsy.

If it is anticipated that this could be a problem, the environment should be adapted to accommodate the needs of the individual.

## Sound

Selected rhythmical music is widely used in conjunction with soft lighting. However, it is sound and the variety of tone, pitch, rhythm and spacing that is important. Other sound effects should also be used, such as bird and animal noises, or wind and rain effects. Sudden loud bangs or extreme variations of pitch would not be used in Snoezelen as these would be alarming and uncomfortable. Musical instruments, activity boards and other items that produce sounds can be used in conjunction with the Snoezelen environment. Electronic sounds can provide a wide range of pitch and volume and can be of value in the room that aims to offer greater choice to the participant.

## Furnishings

These should be kept to a minimum as they can limit choice by suggesting areas where the person should sit. It is better to ensure that the whole area is made as comfortable as possible so that the user can sit or lie anywhere they choose. Selected items such as billowing cushions, water and air mattresses, and floppy islands are of particular value in creating relaxing areas.

Cushions, blankets and fabrics can provide comfortable and stimulating additions to White rooms. These can also help to personalise the environment whilst adding varieties of colour and texture to surfaces.

Ball pools provide valuable tactile stimulation due to the pressure exerted by the individual's own body weight. They are also very comfortable to sit or lie in, adapting to any body posture. Their value in stimulation and relaxation can be increased by enclosing them in light curtains and adding lights and sounds to the room. The effect of this can be very inviting and pleasurable.

## Smell

Smell is a powerful yet often under used sense. Aromatic massage oils, joss sticks, or specially designed smell boxes will provide stimulation and recognition, forming a valuable link and association with the Snoezelen environment.

Pomanders and scented cushions and pillows will provide objects than can be handled whilst stimulating the sense of smell. Experimentation with various smells could develop a valuable library and range of useful and pleasurable experiences.

## Taste

Taste can be included by the use of the wide variety of things that can be spread on bread. Toast soldiers can act as a good base for these whilst biscuits and other small snacks are also valuable.

The endless variety of flavoured drinks can provide additional stimulating and experimentation will help to widen experience.

## Water

Water has been included in a number of Snoezelen centres. Swimming pools can be enhanced by the use of Snoezelen type lighting and sounds whilst a jacuzzi provides valuable tactile stimulation from jets of water and bubbles. Most people enjoy bathing and this can be enhanced in a Snoezelen type atmosphere as the participant needs the direct support of the carer providing valuable attention and communication.

## Developing an enabling approach

Many users of the Snoezelen environment will happily explore their surroundings with confidence and independence. Others may require help to relax or explore in the knowledge that someone is beside them.

In each case it is essential to allow the person the freedom to do as they please. The aim is to create an atmosphere where the person will try out new situations or relax and experience their surroundings. This cannot be achieved if people are tense or pressurised by external expectations.

Introducing a person to Snoezelen for the first time should be done with care as new experiences may take time to absorb.

The effect of gentle lights and sounds, combined with the presence of supportive helpers who share the experience of Snoezelen, will generate greater trust and communication between the users.

It is essential for the carer to be responsive to the communications of participants within the Snoezelen environment. As some people will be unable to move freely, it is necessary to be particularly observant of all communications such as sounds, facial expression and body language. By recognising comfort or discomfort, pleasure or displeasure, it will be possible to provide the most appropriate and rewarding use of the time spent in the Snoezelen environment. This will also give the participant the feedback that they are valued and interesting people in their own right.

As the participant becomes familiar with the environment, they will become more confident. If people prefer to relax in the Snoezelen environment this should be encouraged. This may be a tremendous value in itself and it would also be an appropriate use of the experience.

## How might we use the environment

The Snoezelen environment can be used in a variety of ways from group leisure use to more responsive one-to-one sessions. Many of the major benefits to individuals may come from the additional time and attention given in this way.

## One-to-one

Over recent years it has become apparent that Snoezelen can offer valuable opportunities for building relationships when used on a one-to-one basis. This provides valuable personal contact experience for both people and allows for greater communication. Sessions do not need to be long (15 to 30 minutes), but the participant will benefit from regular attendances. If circumstances allow, sessions could be open ended with no fixed time limit.

## Group use

Many people enjoy the company of others and Snoezelen can encourage this by offering the opportunity for shared experiences. People should be allowed to explore the facility and in this way they can become familiar with the experience. The majority of people relax after 10 to 15 minutes as the Snoezelen experience takes effect. Group sessions could last for up to 45 minutes to one hour, although open ended sessions might be encouraged where possible.

## Are their additional benefits?

As relationships between users and helpers develop within Snoezelen and we focus more on sensory experience and communication, there can be a freeing up of carer/participant relationships.

People are more readily accepted as interesting individuals in their own right as we learn much more about their likes and dislikes.

The Snoezelen concept can expand to other rooms such as the bathroom or bedroom in the form of lighting and sound. For some less conventional users whose favourite places might be corners or corridors, one could consider installing special lighting or seating to enhance their comfort and pleasure.

## "Essentials and basics"

As the Snoezelen concept develops, it is becoming clear that there is no right or wrong way to build a suitable facility. What is clear is that we can maximise the value of a room by providing certain basic effects used in conjunction with a sensitive approach.

As with any developing concept it is likely that we can learn from the positive and negative experiences of others. These notes are intended to five basic advice that is frequently sought by people wishing to develop a Snoezelen room for the first time.

There is a tremendous amount of skill and experience currently held by commercial firms who can design and build Snoezelen rooms. It is through the efforts of one of these companies, Rompa, that the concept was popularised and spread throughout the UK.

The quality of professionally built rooms should direct us, where possible, to secure the funding and engage a design and build a company of good reputation. Whilst the benefits of this approach include safe, functional facilities that have a professional finish, there are other ways of developing facilities. It might be that a staged development starting in one corner of a large room is necessary due to financial constraints. This way extra items of equipment to provide additional effects could be added at a later date. A complete 'home made' environment is also possible, although we should remind ourselves that the development of Snoezelen has offered us the opportunity to provide people who have profound sensory, physical and mental disabilities with high quality facilities that were previously denied to them. It would be a shame to lose this principle in the search for economy. In applying the same principle to leisure facilities for ourselves, we are unlikely to value poorly designed, ill equipped, "do it yourself" facilities. We should aim to provide the best.

Whether we are engaging a professional designer or undertaking our own conversion, it is essential to consider the following:

1    What do the users need?

    a)    Is the user group known?

    b)    Can the design be geared to individuals?

    c)    Will the facilities be used by other known users?

    d)    Does this require a variety of wider effects to select from?

2    What experiences are you planning to provide?

    a)    Relaxation - gentle stimulation

    b)    Choice - user operable devices that stimulate

    c)    Movement - exploration, experience and stimulation

    d)    Sensory - smells, touch, sound, taste, visual

    e)    Sharing - comfort, costly one-to-one, or group activity.

Experience has shown that whilst it is possible to provide a variety of user operable stimulating effects in a White room, the mixture of facilities can destroy the potential of the room for relaxation and stress release through calm, predictable, gentle stimulation.

As White rooms are clearly associated with Snoezelen, it is perhaps better to consider that use operable, noisy equipment is placed outside the room or developed in another room or corridor.

It is essential to plan the room in terms of the needs of the users and the effect required. Care should be taken to ensure that one effect does not destroy another.

Points to consider

1   White rooms provide relaxation, sharing and gentle simulation. They should be safe and promote a feeling of security. No sudden noises, jumping, powerful lights, harsh surfaces or through traffic.

2   Activity rooms/play areas or adventure rooms can provide opportunities for movement, places to hide, noise, robust play and comfort. Use lights and sound to enhance effects.

3   Dark rooms are good for powerful effects from lights and sound using pressure or sound responsive switches.

4   Water areas can provide comfort, contact and security through one-to-one contact. Touch is well served through wet surfaces, bubbles, water jets and temperature changes.

5   Plants provide comfort, smells and texture.

6   Floors can be used for different surface experience through a wide variety of carpet and linoleum coverings.

7   Walls (in the correct facility) can provide tactile experiences by the addition of a wide variety of safe stimulating surfaces.

8   Daylight is normally excluded in white and dark rooms, but can be used to advantage elsewhere by filtering through net, coloured fablon or cellophane.

9   Lights can be used separately or combined to create more effects. It is usually better to use one or two at a time rather than confusing the atmosphere by too many effects.

10  Cushioning on floors and walls is essentially there for comfort and safety. It presents an inviting environment where we can sit or lie down without the restriction of furniture. In large rooms we need to consider the mobility of the user. Leave a firm track across the room if possible. If this is left uncovered (by

foam cushioning) it will be easier for the less ambulant to walk on. The track could be covered by firm carpet to ensure safety whilst providing a surface that does not snag the feet.

11  Ball pools can be surrounded by curtains. Lights and sound can be added converting the pool in to a powerful relaxation area.

## A WHITE ROOM - THE BASICS

Whilst the type and variety of the Snoezelen environment will depend on the factors mentioned earlier, there are some basic design features that are essential for success. More equipment does not mean more success.

1  Access - leave an entrance clear. In large rooms consider a track.
2  Comfort/safety - cushioning - essential on the floor - less essential on walls. Wedges add quality and comfort.
3  Lighting   -   a)  Projector with effect wheels
                             b)  Spot lamps - static - colours
                             c)  Disco spot lamp - changing colours
                             d)  Mirror ball (rotates) - goes with disco spot lamp.
4  Focal point - a bubble tube or fibre optic spray.
5  Sounds - speakers or safely placed tape player (constant play facility).
6  Walls - white or magnolia to reflect pastel shades.
7  Mobiles - add interest and change light effects.

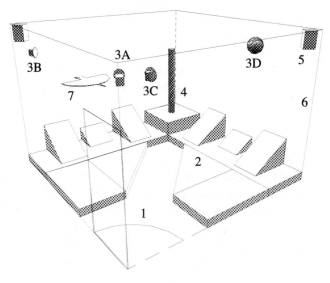

# THE DEVELOPMENT AND EVALUATION OF A SNOEZELEN LEISURE RESOURCE FOR PEOPLE WITH SEVERE MULTIPLE DISABILITY

R. Hutchinson
L. Haggar

## Introduction

In April 1988, planning started for the provision of a Leisure and Recreation resource specifically designed for people with profound multiple disabilities. The concept used was that of Snoezelen, already well established in Holland which involved the creation of a high quality, purpose built environment which would be used in an enthusiastic, caring and sensitive way. The emphasis in Holland was on the provision of a leisure rather than therapeutic environment which included equipment specifically designed for the profoundly disabled individuals enjoyment. March 1990 saw the opening of this leisure environment at Whittington Hall Hospital, Chesterfield, this being the first large scale Snoezelen development in the UK.

The main rationale for developing Snoezelen at Whittington hall was a recognition that one of the basic needs that people have is for leisure and recreation. Recreational activities enable people to recuperate, recuperation being defined by (Cunningham et al 1989) as being "not merely resting, but the feeling of restoration and refreshment which one attains from engaging in stimulating activities which are free from pressure and enjoyed for their own sake". When considering leisure activities for the person with a profound disability there is often an emphasis on the learning or therapeutic dimension of recreation, for example, the acquisition of a new skill or the recommendation of a behaviour problem. The Snoezelen concept, however, stresses the fact that these people have the same right to leisure time as every other individual and whilst therapeutic outcome or skill learning may arise from Snoezelen activities, the major emphasis is placed firmly on pleasure. (Hulsegge and Verhuel 1987)

One can imagine how confusing, threatening and beyond control the normal life of the profoundly disabled person must appear at times. Frequently controlled by others who may be well meaning enough in their intentions, they may be left in environments which are unstimulating from their perspective or simply beyond their comprehension. The content of most television programmes is a good example, yet television is the most frequently recorded pastime for these individuals, (Lambe and Hogg, 1987). They have a primary need for stimulation like all human beings but their disabilities frequently prevent them from expressing and fulfilling this need in an appropriate way. the carer or therapist may also be at a loss for ideas, particularly in the area of leisure. Whilst the concept of normalisation stresses the need for opportunities to access a range of high quality leisure facilities as part of people's lifestyle, no such facilities have been available for this client group. Snoezelen was developed specifically to meet these special needs. The environments offer a range of sensory stimulation which is novel, enjoyable and allow the individual to choose. The chance for human contact, warmth and shared experience is also seen as crucial in Snoezelen, the carer being actively encouraged to participate. The concept also meets criteria associated with normalisation in that Snoezelen facilities may be used in a large centre or brought to a home or ward setting and may be enjoyed by people with or without a disability. Thus this high quality facility can be adapted and enjoyed on a large or small scale, just as the non-disabled person might enjoy a trip to the cinema or watching a video at home.

The word Snoezelen is a composite of the Dutch words for sniff and doze, seeking to capture the concept of sensations and emotions. It starts from the recognition that in development terms, profoundly disabled people interact with their environment primarily through the sensory and motor modalities ensuring that the stimulation provided is appropriate and accessible to the user. They are also functionally operable by profoundly disabled individuals. The environments are presented in an adult way, inviting spontaneous exploration and appealing to the whole person, both sensorily and emotionally. An atmosphere of security and freedom from threat is created by sensitive enabling staff. The essence of Snoezelen is to create a feeling of safety, novelty and stimulation under the users control.

Before the Snoezelen facility was established at Whittington Hall, a team of staff were already providing Snoezelen type activities for profoundly disabled residents. This team comprised both trained nursing staff and unqualified 'therapy workers', all of whom shared a commitment to working with this client group and some of whom had been recruited specifically for this purpose. Activities included relaxation, aromatherapy, a wide variety of sensory stimulation, boisterous play in the 'Rumpus Room' and working with residents on a large inflatable structure. All of these activities had provided popular with residents and the team placed great emphasis on building up relationships and sharing experiences during sessions. They also felt it was a basic right of the residents to participate in enjoyable activities purely for their own sake rather than for therapeutic purposes. The teams approach helped them to gain the most out of sensory, relaxation and play sessions.

Before the centre opened, the Snoezelen team received extensive in-house training in sensory integration techniques, stimulation and facilitating improved communication with residents. This took the form of experimental workshops where an emphasis was placed on participation and sharing of ideas. These workshops built upon the skills that team members already possessed. They were led by staff from Speech Therapy, Physiotherapy, Occupational Therapy and Psychology from within the service. The aim was to equip the Snoezelen team with a range of skills that would be used in a creative and imaginative way, enabling clients to gain the maximum enjoyment from the Snoezelen environment. Many of the exercises included communicating emotion via touch and experiencing the surrounding environment and interactions whilst sensorily disabled. This type of exercise sensitised the Snoezelen team to some of the experiences and limitations that a severely disabled person may experience.

**Enabling**

The enabling attitude is central to the concept of Snoezelen and can be described as a 'sensitive, caring, non-directive approach in which an atmosphere of safety and security is created and free choice encouraged', (Haggar). It is expected that the enabler when involved with a client, will share a common positive emotional experience with that client.

Enabling does not focus on therapeutic outcome but rather its focus is to assist users in gaining maximum pleasure from the Snoezelen facility.

For this to occur, managers need to 'enable' their staff to work as 'enablers' in the Snoezelen setting through the presence of appropriate support to their staff; active involvement of enablers in the organisation and administration of the Snoezelen environment, and the adoption of strategies which recognise and reduce the stress the staff experience as enablers.

The enabling approach used in the Snoezelen setting can be transferred in to the clients 'care' environment as the use of sensory activity and the development of an 'intimate' relationship with the client in the Snoezelen setting will only have lasting benefit if the client can enjoy similar experiences in the "ordinary world". This can be achieved by incorporating creative, sensory activity into the clients everyday world, the client sharing their experience of this activity with those providing care and support. The client is enabled to share the intimate moments of everyday life to support their need for dependency,independency and expression. Most people are dependent on others for contact at bed time, meal time and are dependent on others for withdrawal and privacy. We need others to allow us to be independent in making decisions, increasing our freedom and choices. Friends and colleagues are necessary for us to express and confide out thoughts and feelings of personal inadequacy, fears for the future, despair, difficulty in coping with authority and our feelings of success. Enabling allows the client not only the **RECEIVE** support but also to **GIVE** support to others, to peers and to carers. This transforms care into a **DYNAMIC, LIBERATING** human experience. We do not get our sense of value by receiving from others but by sharing the giving and receiving experiences. The person with a profound disability must be enabled to give to those around them.

Within the enabling relationship, we must take account of those experiences, memories, ambitions and sensations that influence the persons behaviour at a particular point in time. We are all influenced by what is happening now, what happened yesterday, last week, last year in our life.Also, what we feel will happen today, tomorrow, next week, in the future. What happened previously or what will happen in the future may have much more influence upon our behaviour than our current situation. We must take account of a persons **LIFE SPACE** (REDL. 1965). Similarly, we must take account of the persons **LIFE SPACE INTERACTIONS** . Those relationships with carers in the clients environment which the clients experiences as significant. The relationship may be one that the person experienced previously, or may be one that the person will experience in the future. It may be what our parents or teacher said to us on a particular occasion; it may be experience of sustained abuse; it may be that a particular nurse is especially caring when we are in pain; it may be what the doctor may say tomorrow; it may be looking forward to the return of our partner from a business trip; it may be waiting for an agitated client to pick on me as I am less able and turn my wheelchair over. Life space interactions have an immediate and a lasting effect.

An approach to care in which these factors are explicitly addressed is **SOCIAL EDUCATION.** Within this approach, creative sensory activities are used to help to release tension, express feeling, develop self confidence, encourage exploration and promote choice. As they share much of the life of clients, workers become involved in a wide range of creative sensory activities which are not ends to themselves, but rather constitute the means by which workers and clients develop the shared interests and understanding that enable growth to happen. Workers are usually highly motivated to take part which helps in the creation of a purposeful way of life in a setting where apathy and despair could become all that clients and workers had to look forward to. This approach seeks the **JUDICIOUS** use of Occupational Therapy, Nursing, Physiotherapy, Psychology, Speech Therapy, Medicine and Psychiatry to enhance the opportunities created for client personal growth. The approach seeks a balance between a therapeutic orientation, a task orientation, and a leisure orientation. Some activity has as a focus, warmth and empathy; some guidance and direction with an expectation of change, and some is leisure orientated, is non directive, promoting sharing and rapport with an expectation of pleasure.

NOTE: Social Education Reference - Jones, HD, The Social Educator in Western Europe - in Thompson, T. and Mathias P, Standards and Mental Handicap - Keys to Competence, Bailliere Tindall, ISBN 0 7020-1566-0 (1992).

Life Space: Redl F and Wineman D, Controls from Within, Free Press, New York (1995).

Dutch workers have stressed the need for centres to be staffed by the 'right kind of people'. The team comprising of eight individuals and a Sister were picked to staff Snoezelen as they shared this enabling attitude and approach.

An operational policy was drawn up, emphasising the use of Snoezelen as a leisure facility. Whilst it was recognised that therapeutic and educational objectives could be met within the centre, staff wishing to use it this way would be asked to maintain the normal Snoezelen principles and leisure would usually be given priority. It was agreed that all staff and visitors to the centre would be expected to participate in activities and all activities were to be co-ordinated through the Snoezelen team.

After the centre opened, a quality control circle was set up to meet on a regular basis. It was recognised that there is constant change and growth within a high quality facility such as Snoezelen and the circle aimed to promote the continuing evolution of good practice within the facility.

## THE CENTRE

The Snoezelen facility comprises six specially adapted areas which combine to provide a comprehensive library of stimulation.

1    **The Adventure Room**

This is a large, colourful, soft room containing a variety of shapes and spaces. It is designed for adventurous and robust activity, although some residents prefer to relax quietly in the ball pool.

2    **Jacuzzi**

This room consists of a large jacuzzi pool in pleasant surroundings which provides sensory experience through the soothing and massaging effects of water.

3    **Sitting Room**

This open area is for waiting, taking snacks or simply doing nothing, perhaps after a boisterous session.

4    **Sound and Light Room**

This room has state of the art technology in light and sound which can be controlled by even the most disabled user. Specially adapted switches can produce stunning visual displays and sound effects whilst a vibrating floor is available for tactile stimulation.

5    **Touch Corridor**

This passage contains a variety of tactile experiences where people can explore shapes and textures.

6    **White Room**

This large room is designed for deep relaxation. Lights, soft music and comfortable fittings create a feeling of calm enjoyment and security.

There are also facilities to stimulate smell and taste and various 'activity boards' scattered throughout the centre. The Snoezelen team have sought to personalise the environments by adding various items such as hanging mobiles, furry cushions and colourful tactile collages for the walls.

Snoezelen facilities have also been established at a local hostel and in community bungalow settings. Staff's experience with, and enthusiasms about these facilities, suggest that this type of activity can work on a smaller scale and can also be brought into the home.

## ACTIVITIES

The Centre is used in a variety of ways. Regular sessions are time-tabled where groups of residents attend, exploring and relaxing within the facility. Individual sessions are also available where one-to-one contact enables staff to meet particular residents' needs more sensitively than in a group situation. Carers from the wards and relatives are encouraged to attend and participate in group sessions or individual work. Casual use by residents who are able to make their own way to the centre is also encouraged providing this does not hinder other users. At present, one morning a week is kept free for use by paramedics and clients involved with local community mental handicap teams. Funding made available for extra staff has allowed the centre to be opened in the evening and at weekends. Sunday afternoon opening is specifically for children with a disability and their parents.

As Snoezelen is a leisure resource, it should ideally be as accessible to a disabled person as any local leisure centre is to a non-disabled person.


## RESEARCH BACKGROUND

A number of subjective views held by the Dutch workers about the value of Snoezelen as a leisure resource led to the development of a research project in parallel with the development of the facility at Whittington Hall. This twelve month project sought to evaluate the impact of Snoezelen on the daily lives of the residents and staff who used it. The Dutch workers had resisted formal evaluation procedures fearing this would force the environments into a more therapeutic, objective and product orientated dimension. However, it can be argued that research can positively contribute to the refinement and development of work in this area and also formally demonstrate Snoezelen's worth to other workers in the field who are considering investing in a similar facility. It was felt a balance could be achieved between research and retaining the fundamental ethic of Snoezelen as a leisure resource rather than a therapeutic activity. The essence of the research was to capture the experience of users and answer questions raised in a holistic and qualitative manner. Such questions included: Do profoundly disabled users enjoy their time in Snoezelen? Are they able to relax during Snoezelen time? What is the impact of Snoezelen on the client-carer relationship?

The literature in the area of leisure activities for profoundly disabled individuals is sparse, and whist writers have a greed these individuals have a born right to, and a need for leisure (eg Lyons, 1986) ideas for appropriate facilities have not been prolific. Staff at Whittington Hall had been carrying out sensory, relaxation and play activities including use of an inflatable structure with residents before the advent of Snoezelen and felt these activities were enjoyed by and of benefit to residents. Some writers have focused on the benefits of sensory stimulation with this client group (eg Glover and Mesibov, 1978, Prosser 1988, Norris 1982) and the use of inflatable structure has also been explored (Crisp et al, 1984; Sykes et al, 1985). However, research in this area has been focused almost exclusively on therapeutic or educational outcome where as the emphasis of Snoezelen is firmly on clients' pleasure.

As Snoezelen was a new and innovative concept, the research was by nature exploratory and descriptive. It was anticipated that, as with any new system, work within the centre would evolve with the experience of staff and users, therefore, there was a need for a flexible research design which would evolve in parallel with the facility. It was felt that a qualitative study would enable issues to be explored in a real life setting and that more quantitative work was inappropriate at this stage, particularly in the light of ethical and practical considerations. The points outlined by Marshall and Rossman, 1989 (p.144-149) were adopted as criteria by which to judge the research design.


## METHODOLOGY

Three main methods of data were used:

    i)    Observation data involving kinetic analysis

    ii)    Interviews with staff

    iii)    Collection of quantitative data

The project was designed to address the following questions:

    a)    Do clients find enjoyment, stimulation and relaxation in Snoezelen?

    b)    Do clients make independent choice and express preferences in Snoezelen?

    c)    Is the amount of time a client spends off the ward by attending Snoezelen increased?

    d)    Does the client have a wider choice of activities when attending Snoezelen?

    e)    Are there any behavioural changes in the client when in Snoezelen and do these generalise?

    f)    Do staff gain increased knowledge about the client they work with?

g) Does the quality of the relationship between staff and client improve whilst sharing Snoezelen time?

h) Do staff feel that individual benefit from Snoezelen?

## Selection of Sample

A pool of potential users was drawn containing a number of individuals with a range of disabilities, most of whom had attended the sensory, relaxation and play sessions on a regular basis prior to Snoezelen. Within this pool, clusters of individuals with specific disabilities (eg non ambulant, sensory deficits) and/or particular problems (eg self injurious behaviour, stereo-typical behaviour) were identified. Fifteen individuals were chosen randomly from the various clusters in an attempt to represent the diversity of the population of users. Their disabilities are briefly described in Table 1.

# RANGE OF DISABILITIES IN THE SAMPLE

| Speech | Ambulant | Sensory Handicap | Challenging | Other |
|--------|----------|------------------|-------------|-------|
| W No | Yes - crawl shuffle | No | Yes - Head bangs, smacks face bites self | Sib* Head |
| C No | No | No | No | Severe EP* Severe Spasticity |
| D No | No | No | Yes - picks fingers pushes finger up nose | Sib Stereotypies EP Rocks |
| P No | Yes - walks | Very light sensitive eyes from cataract operations | No | Temporal Lobe EP |
| J No | No | Partially Blind | No | |
| G No | Yes - shuffles | No | No | Rheumatism in leg |
| B Elective Mute | No | No | No | Manic depressive illness, severe anxiety |
| T No | Yes - walks | No | Yes Autism | Autistic character Assoc. stereotypies twirls, rocks |
| J Yes | No | No | No | Hydrocephalus |
| D No | No | Blind | No | Autistic character rocks, withdrawn |
| N No | Yes - walks | No | Yes Autism Assoc. | Autistic character rocks, paces, stamps |
| B Yes | Yes - walks | No | Yes - | Very able Tantrums Seeking |

KEY: *SIB = Self injurious behaviour    *EP = Epilepsy

*TABLE 1*

Information about each individual was collected by the research before Snoezelen opened; and over a three month period during which each individual attended regular Snoezelen sessions. At the end of this period by comparing this information individuals would, in effect, act as their own controls. The selection of a separate control group was not considered as it would involve denying individuals access to the centre.

Kinesics - The Portrait Sheet and Diary Card

Kinesics is defined as the study of body motion communication (Birdwhistell, 1970). Where kinesic analysis is used in qualitative research, it is frequently to give the researcher confidence about the accuracy of information provided by a subject in the degree of congruency between the subjects words and body language. A somewhat different approach was taken in this study, one of the main functions of which was to decide whether a group of profoundly disabled individuals found the Snoezelen environments enjoyable, stimulating and/or relaxing. With the non disabled person experiencing a new leisure research, one would simply ask how they felt about it. As only two individuals in the research sample had significant expressive language skills it appeared some form of kinesic analysis was necessary to obtain the user's point of view.

The 'portrait sheet' was devised to provide the researcher both with a character sketch of each individual in the sample and the main behavioural cues by which they communicated mood stares and interest (see Appendix 1 for example). Information for each portrait sheet was obtained from two identified key workers who had worked closely with the individual and knew them well. One key worker was identified from the ward, and one from the Snoezelen team. Members of the latter had previously constituted the 'therapies' team who had provided the sensory, relaxation and play sessions which are described more fully in the first section of this text. The information was obtained by means of a structured interview which is described shortly and was held before individuals began attending Snoezelen.

Key workers for each individual were asked how each communicated the following:

Happiness/Sadness
Agitation/Relaxation
Interest/Disinterest

When responses were compared between ward and Snoezelen workers for each individual, levels of agreement on these cues was found to be virtually 100%, thus it was felt that the measure could be taken as robust. There is some empirical evidence, although not specifically in the area of profound disability, that carers who know individuals well are able to interpret non verbal cues to mood states more accurately than trained observers (eg Fraser and Orzois, 1981). Certainly it emerged that most individuals in the sample were able to communicate their moods states effectively to key workers and that means of communication were often highly idiosyncratic. It also emerged that staff were sensitive to the communicative value of subtle behavioural cues and reported these. Two members of staff who knew the individuals well appeared to be making the same interpretations of the same behavioural cues.

Individuals' particular disabilities and problems were also recorded on the portrait sheet, as was a brief description of their character. The researcher sought to provide a holistic picture of each individual so the impact of Snoezelen on their daily lives could be assessed.

The 'diary card' was designed in conjunction with the portrait sheet as a non intrusive means of collecting observational data during Snoezelen sessions (see Appendix 2 for example). A card was completed by Snoezelen staff each time an individual attended Snoezelen over a three month period which commenced when the centre opened. Staff were instructed to record the following information:

*       Dominant mood in Snoezelen as interpreted from behaviour cues
        observed.

*       Whether a change of mood occurred during the session and the
        nature of any such change.

*       Whether a choice was made or a preference expressed.

*       Time spent in each Snoezelen room (refer to earlier text for
        descriptions of rooms) and total time spent in environment.

*       Type of session. Most individuals in the sample attended both
        group sessions and individual sessions on a regular basis, and
        whilst one to one staff attention is guaranteed in the latter, it is not
        usually available in the former.

*       Any other information they felt pertinent.

The concept of 'Snoezeling' was also included which is loosely defined by the Dutch workers as the extent to which the user becomes involved in, or absorbed by the environments. The researcher had originally planned to use the concept of engagement

29

(Felce et al 1985) as a measure of client interest and absorption, however, this was abandoned for several reasons. Firstly, engagement is essentially a quantitative measure and did not appear to fit with the exploratory and descriptive nature of the project.

Secondly, it would have been difficult for valid comparisons to be drawn between levels of engagement in Snoezelen and other environments. Most individuals in the sample spent the majority of their time in unstimulating word environments where there is little opportunity for engagement. Thirdly, there is an implicit assumption that disengagement is a bad thing and whilst this may be the case where lack of resource prevent opportunity for engagement, it is not necessarily so in a leisure environment. Much of the literature in mental handicap implies that these individuals should always be involved in some kind of activity (eg ref. The Activities Catalogue). The Snoezelen environment encourages free choice and if an individual wishes to spend his or her leisure time doing nothing, it is the business of no one to judge the merits of this choice.

'Snoezeling' was therefore, introduced as a qualitative (and non judgmental) alternative to engagement, specific to the environment. Diary cards were completed for individuals by both key and other enabling staff and by the researcher over the designated three month period.

## Staff interviews

Interviews where chosen for this study because of their particular strengths in allowing the researcher to obtain a large amount of information quickly, providing an opportunity for clarification and also for follow up (Marshall & Rossman). The researcher had considered using questionnaires to obtain staff perspectives, however, when a short pilot study was carried out with both techniques, it was found interviews yielded more information and avoided the problem of data loss through non return.

Two structured interviews were carried out with identified key workers for each individual in the sample, one from the ward and one from the Snoezelen team.

The first interview was carried out shortly before the centre opened and the second after the centre had been open for three months. They were conducted in a relaxed and friendly manner with a standardised introduction and prompts. They were constructed to obtain a variety of information, most specifically the following:

i)   Information about each individual in the sample to enable a
     portrait sheet to be constructed after the initial interview.

ii)     Information to establish whether qualitative and/or behavioural changes had emerged in the individuals at follow up, in sessions and/or on the ward.

iii)    Information about the relationship between the interviewee and the individual.

iv)     How the member of staff felt about their job, including information about particular sources of satisfaction and stress.

v)      How the member of staff felt about Snoezelen initially and at follow up, how much they knew about the facility initially and how much they learned at follow up, and to what extent it had influenced their daily working lives at follow up.

The initial and follow up interview were virtually identical in structure so valid responses comparisons could be made and any changes recorded. Some additional questions were also included in the follow up interview which were inappropriate initially, eg a specific request for staff opinion on how they felt the facility could be improved.

Additional information was used to compensate for the limitations and weakness of the technique as described by Marhsall and Rossman. Specifically, the diary cards were included as sources of observational data to be compared and checked for congruency with interview responses. In addition, a period prior to data collection was used as an opportunity for the research to gain staff co-operation and generally establish herself as a familiar face with participants. All interviews were conducted by the researcher. Seven of the eight Snoezelen team members and fourteen ward staff were interviewed, some on more than one occasion when individuals in the sample had the same key worker. In these instances, only sections of the interview pertaining to the individuals in the sample were conducted more than once. Thirty initial and thirty follow up interviews were conducted in total.

## Data to Establish Pattern of Usage

This was collected over a three month period by the Snoezelen team and included the following:

Numbers of residents attending regularly
Numbers of ward staff attending regularly
Use of rooms

Numbers and types of sessions provided by the team
Numbers of cancellations of sessions and whether time
then taken by other users
Community use

## Results

## Data Loss

Three ward key workers had been replaced by other staff preventing valid follow up interviews from being held at the end of the three month data collection period. One member of the sample suffered major and traumatic changes to her life and did not attend sessions as anticipated. Numbers in the final analysis were therefore as follows:

Individual        -      14
Ward Key Workers    -      10
Snoezelen Team Members   -      7

## Analysis of Data

Information from interviews was summarised and comparisons drawn between initial and follow up responses. Information from completed diary cards was tabulated and checked for congruency with follow up interviews responses from the Snoezelen team. It was apparent that diary cards had not been completed for every session attended by each individual, however, in most cases, cards had been completed for the majority of sessions. A high degree of congruency was established in every case. Whilst key enablers had been designated particular individuals, they did not always work with the individuals in Snoezelen and in many cases other team members had completed cards. There was a concern that team members would be anxious to portray Snoezelen in an exaggeratedly rosy light in view of their own enthusiasm for the concept. However, content of certain diary cards indicated that this had not been the case and instances of individuals negative mood states in Snoezelen (eg agitated, disinterested) were reported.

## Enjoyment, Stimulation and Relaxation in Snoezelen (Table 2)

This was established from follow up interview responses by Snoezelen team members and from completed diary cards. All individuals in the sample found Snoezelen enjoyable and were able to relax in the environments. Twelve found the environments stimulating, eg they expressed interest, played actively, explored etc.

## Independent Choice and Expression of Preference in Snoezelen (Table 2)

This was established from follow up interviews responses by Snoezelen team members and from completed diary cards. Independent choice is defined as where an individual enters or leaves an environment of his/her own volition or approaches apiece of equipment. All seven ambulant or partially mobile individuals in the sample were observed by staff to make independent choices on a regular basis. Of the remaining 7 non ambulant individuals, 6 expressed preferences for particular environments or stimuli.

|  | Yes | No | Don't know |
|---|---|---|---|
| Stimulation | 12 | 2 | - |
| Relaxation | 14 | - | - |
| Enjoyment | 14 | - | - |
| Independent Choice | All Ambulant or partially mobile 7 | All non Ambulant 7 | - - |
| Preference Expressed | 13 | - | 1 |

*TABLE 2 - (N = 14)*

## Time Off Ward and Choice of Activities

This was established from comparisons of ward records before and after the centre had opened. The sensory, play and relaxation sessions offered before Snoezelen were defined as leisure and were in fact virtually the only recreational pursuits available regularly to the more profoundly disabled individuals in the sample. They averaged two hours time off ward weekly. The centre provided more time off the ward for 11 individuals in the sample and a greater choice of activities for all but 2. However, it should be pointed out that the increased time off the ward amounted to only an extra hour weekly for most individuals.

## Behavioural and/or Qualitative Changes (Appendix 3)

This was established from comparison of initial and follow up interview responses, by both Snoezelen workers and ward key workers providing the latter had not changed during the three month period. Snoezelen workers had worked with all individuals in sensory, relaxation and play sessions prior to the centre opening, and could therefore make subjective comparisons of individuals responses in these sessions with responses in Snoezelen. They reported 'positive' changes in 11 individuals, negative changes in 1 and no change in 2. Broadly speaking, a positive change includes examples where more pleasure is expressed, relaxation is achieved more quickly or without staff help, greater interest is expressed, behavioural problems such as self injury decreases, all in comparison to staffs' previous experiences with the individuals. A negative change would include an increase in behaviour problems, an increase in agitation, whilst 'no change' is recorded where staff cannot perceive a difference in the individual.

The same criteria for positive and negative changes were applied to ward staff responses Here ward key workers reported any change they had observed in the individual on the ward since they had started attending Snoezelen. In some cases, changes had emerged but ward staff felt unsure whether these were directly related to Snoezelen or attributable to other factors.

## Generalisation to Ward

This was established from comparison of initial and follow up interview responses by ward key workers, and expands on the previous section. A positive generalisation was reported in four cases and a negative generalisation in one case. Criteria for positive and negative are as detailed earlier. It should be stressed that this is only recorded when ward staff state that they feel any change in the individual is related to Snoezelen attendance.

## Staff 'Insight' Into Individuals

The term 'insight' is used broadly, being seen as present when a person had learned something new or expanded their existing knowledge about the individual in the sample, and his or her needs. Suggestions of 'insight' was established from comparisons of initial and follow up interview responses by Snoezelen and ward key workers. 'Insight' is only recorded when interviewees stated at follow up that they had learned something new about the individual or when a striking difference in response content was noted when comparing initial and follow up interviews (7 team and 2 ward staff).

## Quality of Relationship Between Staff and Individual

Initial and follow up interview responses by Snoezelen and ward key workers were compared and reported of improved noted. In every case, where relationships were reported to have improved in quality suggestions of staff' insight' into individuals also emerged. This occurred with 7 team and 2 ward staff.

## Staff feelings about benefits from Snoezelen to individuals in sample

This was established from responses at follow up interviews by Snoezelen and ward key workers where 'positive, specific to Snoezelen' is recorded. Staff have described benefits perceived in individuals and related these benefits specifically to the environments. Some staff have described perceived benefits which they feel could be gained from other environments. It should be stressed that these sections represent only brief summaries of the volumes of data obtained on each individual in the sample. The following is an attempt to summarise staff feelings in the facility.

## The Snoezelen Team

The initial and follow up interviews included sections on sources of stress and difficulty at work. Whilst there were great individual differences, the most commonly reported source at follow up was ward staff attitude with 6 out of 7 members expressing feelings of disappointment or frustration at lack of co-operation, enthusiasm, participation and support from ward staff. However, where particular wards had been involved, the relationships between staff and team members appeared to have improved. The section of sources of job satisfaction yielded mainly 'resident related' and 'team related' responses both initially and at follow up. Common responses included 'seeing residents enjoying themselves', 'watching residents expressions' and 'working in a team which feels like a family'. Responses at follow up strongly suggest these sources had been enhanced by the Snoezelen environment, with examples such as 'achieving quicker breakthroughs', 'being able to provide an extra personal touch' and 'the team feels closer'. All team members had attended training workshops prior to working in Snoezelen with 2 members visiting Holland. All were aware of the Snoezelen philosophy before the centre opened and all stated that they had learned something new after working in the environment. Examples of new learning included 'my eyes have been opened to residents characters and how these can change in Snoezelen', 'I feel Snoezelen can give insight into people'. All the team felt positively and were enthusiastic about the concept at initial interview. Comments made at three month follow up strongly indicated that enthusiasm had been maintained and in many cases, increased. The environment appeared to have stimulated many new ideas amongst team members and had lived up to, or in some cases, outstripped the high expectation expressed in the initial interview. Thus Snoezelen appears to have made a positive impact on the teams daily working lives.

## Ward Key Workers

All ward staff interviewed gave the response of staff shortages and related problems as the major source of job stress both initially and at follow up. Several stated that they have been unable to become involved with Snoezelen sessions because of this. After follow up, two wards appeared to have adopted the concept and were attending sessions with residents and attempting to provide other leisure activities. Amongst key workers from these wards, changes emerged at follow up in sources of job stress and satisfaction with fewer 'resident related' included in the former ('eg 'noise', 'constant vigilance', 'behaviour problems' ') and more 'resident related' sources included in the latter (eg 'seeing residents relaxed', 'helping personalities develop', 'taking on holiday without major behaviour problems'). One of these wards housed residents with challenging behaviour and it is certainly worth commenting that the ward sister and staff felt all residents had shown a reduction in challenging behaviours after three months f regular Snoezelen sessions. It was felt that noise levels had decreased on the ward and residents seemed happier and more relaxed in themselves.

Initially, the majority of ward staff interviewed were aware that Snoezelen was a leisure resource and half knew that it involved 'sensory stimulation'. Only one who had visited Holland, seemed aware of the philosophy and only one had looked round the centre prior to opening. Five expressed a desire to become involved. At follow up 7 had looked round, 3 described 'Snoezeling' and 5 had learned something new about the facility.

Initially, 7 ward staff felt positive about and expressed enthusiasm for the facility and this number remained the same at follow up. However, changes had occurred in the individuals expressing these feelings. One particular ward appeared dissatisfied with the way the centre was run and responses at follow up were clearly affected by the desire for more sessions. It is worth noting that this ward already had more session time than any other! Also, the desire to more time suggested that staff felt residents were benefiting in some way although some would not comment on this. At follow up, workers from those wards who had become involved and embraced the concept felt most positively about the facility and expressed the most enthusiasm. They reported examples of positive generalisation amongst residents and were themselves perceived in a positive light by Snoezelen workers. Workers from the challenging behaviour ward expressed a desire to expand Snoezelen activities on the ward and were in the process of setting up a relaxation room at the follow up.

## Data to establish pattern of use

Table 3 shows average numbers of residents attending sessions weekly, type of session timetables and average lengths of these sessions. Table 4 details hours of Snoezelen time offered to wards. The centre was open from 8.30am to 3.30pm, Monday to Friday, and staffed by 7 full-time members of staff, one part-time worker and a co-ordinator in charge. Group and individual sessions for residents on each ward were timetabled. Tuesday mornings were kept free for use by hospital paramedics and community groups and bookings were taken for this time.

Records of ward staff attendance, cancellations and wards taking advantage of cancellations were found to be incomplete at the end of the data collection period. Informal discussions with the co-ordinator indicated that numbers for all three compared favourably with those for activities offered by the team before the centre opened.

| Ward & No. Residents | No. attending | Group sessions | 1-1 (1 hour each) |
|---|---|---|---|
| Ashford -14<br>All HD* | All + 1<br>alternative<br>(1hr) | 2 weekly (2hrs) | 6 weekly |
| Ashbourne - 12<br>Majority HD | 11 | 2 weekly (2hrs) | 6 weekly |
| Hayfield - 17<br>All HD | 14 | 2 weekly (2hrs each) | 11 weekly |
| Gosforth - 23<br>HD & Elderly | 9<br>(Remaining are older residents) | 2 weekly (1.25hrs and 2hrs) | 3 weekly |
| Curbar - 13<br>Majority HD | 10 | 1 weekly (1.25hrs) | 3 weekly |
| Edensor - 20<br>Majority Elderly | 2 | 1 weekly (1.25hrs) | 2 weekly |
| Somersall - 8<br>Majority Elderly | 3 | 1 weekly (1.25hrs) | - |
| Beeley - 15 | 5 | 1 weekly (2hrs) | 2 weekly |
| Dale<br>STC* | Variable | All 1-1 | Varies with staff/cancellations available |
| Rhead House - 11<br>Challenging Beh | All | 1 alternative (1hr) | 30 weekly |
| Totals (not including or paramedics/ community) | 84 | 14 (approx 120 residents | 70 sessions/ residents |

*HD = High Dependancy
*STC = Short Term Care
TABLE 3

## Snoezelen Times per Week (hours)

| | |
|---|---|
| Ashford | 10 + 1 alternative week |
| Ashbourne | 10 |
| Hayfield | 15 |

| | |
|---|---|
| Gosforth | 12.25 |
| Curbar | 4.25 |
| Edensor | 3.25 |
| Somersall | 1.25 |
| Furniss | 2.25 |
| Beeley | 4 |
| Rhead House | 30 + 1 alternative weekly |
| Paramedics/Community | 2 |
| Total | 95.25 hours |

*TABLE 4*

Use of rooms was recorded. The adventure room, a large soft play are with ballpool, optikinetic displays and various activity boards was found to be used the most. This was probably because large groups of residents can be more comfortably contained within this room with a minimum of staff supervision, and individuals can choose from boisterous or relaxing activities. The White room, a relaxation area with comfortable fittings and many optikinetic displays was the second most widely used room. Numbers were restricted to two staff and two residents for safety purposes. The light and sound room and the tactile corridor appeared to be areas for 'passing through', where residents explored on their way to the other environments. Whilst not a specific Snoezelen environment, the sitting area was found to be used as a pleasant waiting area at the beginning and end of almost every session. Casual users (eg individuals arriving at the centre without a timetabled session) were also found to choose it as an area for socialisation and the team used it as an area for meetings and informal discussions. No data was kept on the amount of casual use. Residents were permitted to wander through the centre providing they did not disrupt other users and a number were found to take advantage of this, including ambulant residents from the challenging behaviour ward and some elderly residents. It also emerged that some elderly residents for whom staff had felt Snoezelen was not appropriate, had asked to attend and tier wishes had been catered for. The white room and jacuzzi appear to be most popular with elderly residents. The time allotted on Tuesday morning for paramedic and community use was booked several months in advance. Many community groups returned for regular sessions. Physiotherapy staff were using the jacuzzi areas on a weekly basis. Regular community users included groups of disabled adults and children, and individuals with challenging behaviour, all of whom attended with carers.

## Discussion

The findings detailed in this paper strongly suggest that Snoezelen is of value as a leisure resource for profoundly disabled individuals and broadly speaking, lends support to the Dutch workers subjective opinions. The 14 individuals followed all enjoyed using the facility and were able to relax in the environments. Individuals who could walk or move around exercised choice. It could be argued that these more severely disabled individuals were making a choice, as by communicating their preferences behaviourally to staff, staff ensured they were taken to preferred areas of taken out of areas they expressed dislike for. This has important connotations, as it is has been demonstrated that continuous involvement in situations with no opportunity for choice may result in feelings of helplessness (Seligman, 1975). This learned helplessness may result in withdrawal which makes an individual appear more disabled than they actually are. (Dattilo & Rusch, 1985). A high incidence of learned helplessness occurs amongst individuals who are rarely provided with opportunities to exhibit self determined behaviours (Floors & Rosen, 1975) and severely disabled individuals are probably one of the most vulnerable groups (Guess et al, 1985).

Provision of leisure activities where an element of choice is available could help to prevent or ameliorate learned helplessness amongst this client group (Iso-Ahola et al, 1980). Choice is fundamental to the Snoezelen concept.

Qualitative and behavioural changes of a positive nature were described in 11 individuals during session by Snoezelen staff and these changes appeared to generalise to individual's ward environments in at least four cases. In most of these cases, ward staff had embraced the Snoezelen concept and become involved with Snoezelen sessions. Whilst no definite conclusions can be drawn from this study, information from initial and follow up interviews indicated that these ward staff may have changed the way in which they perceived their role as carers. Rather than feeling they were there to provide basic care, some responses indicated that they had become more sensitive to individuals personal needs, (eg client's right to leisure) and were attempting to facilitate these needs outside the Snoezelen environment. There is clearly a need for further research in this area as Snoezelen may hold potential to change staff attitude and perhaps help 'institutionalised' staff to become more sensitive to individual needs.

A particularly striking change was reported by staff from the challenging behaviour ward, where it was felt that all residents were calmer since attending Snoezelen. It is recognised that bizarre and disturbed behaviours can emerge in both disabled and non disabled individuals when they are exposed to prolonged periods of unvaried stimulation (eg Solomon et al, 1961) and that environmental enrichment can assist in the amelioration of such behaviours (eg Kreger, 1971). Lack of staffing and resources can result in a life of unvarying monotony for the disabled individual, particularly when they live in an institution, and challenging behaviours may exempt such individuals from a move into a community setting with higher staffing ratios and more opportunity for stimulation. It appears Snoezelen may be particularly helpful to these individuals and there is clearly a need for further research to explore the potential of the facility in this area.

The facility appears to have made a positive impact on the daily working lives of the Snoezelen team. Ward staff who became involved also felt positively about Snoezelen, some reporting positive changes in residents, which may reflect their own involvement and possible change in attitude.

However, in the hospital there is clearly a need for more ward based staff to become involved. The centre is shortly to be opened at evenings and weekends to enable them to attend with residents. This additional opening will also increase access to the facility for both residents and disabled individuals in the community. Timetabling of sessions has also allowed individuals with special needs to gain one-to-one staff attention in regular individual sessions. Some of these individuals were included in the sample of fourteen, and whilst staff felt that sessions of this nature were beneficial, such attention does not appear to be a pre-requisite for individuals to enjoy and benefit from the Snoezelen environments.

## Does Snoezelen Work?

This is the question most frequently asked of those involved with Snoezelen. The answer is "for whom?". All 14 individuals followed in this study enjoyed their sessions and as Snoezelen is essentially a leisure resource, it appears to be working for them. It is hoped that future workers in the field will not feel obliged to justify the existence of Snoezelen purely in terms of therapeutic outcome; although such outcomes appear to have emerged in many of the individuals followed. However, the fundamental question is "Do we justify our own leisure pursuits in terms of their therapeutic value?". Certainly pursuits as diverse as playing an energetic sport, watching television and write creatively may all produce therapeutic results, although perhaps such results are better described as 'positive side effects'. These could range from skill learning and increasing world knowledge to stress reduction and relaxation. The reader is invited to imagine the 'negative side effects' which would no doubt affect them if they were denied their favourite leisure pursuit. Such activities are chosen primarily because we enjoy them. The profoundly disabled individual is frequently unable to make this choice independently but this does not mean they have no right to leisure for its own sake. If we value these individuals, it is our responsibility to afford them the same opportunities and access to high quality leisure activities that we enjoy. The findings reported in this paper strongly suggest that there is a place for Snoezelen within this choice.

## REFERENCES

1       Birdwhistell R L. Kinesics and content: Essays on body motion communication.. Philadelphia: University of Pennsylvania Press (1970)

2       Crisp A G. Some evaluations of toy apparatus for severe and profoundly mentally handicapped people. Int. J Rehab Research 7, 431-34 (1984)

3       Cunningham C, Hutchinson E, Kewin J. Recreation for people with profound and severe learning difficulties. The Whittington Hall Snoezelen Project: Whittington Hall Hospital, Old Whittington, Chesterfield (1989).

4       Dattilo J and Rusch F R. Effects of choice on leisure participation for persons with severe handicap. J.A.S.H. 306-11 (1985).

5       Felce D, de Kock U, Saxby H, Thomas M. Small homes for severely and profoundly mentally handicapped adults. Final Report University of Southampton, Department of Psychology (1985).

6       Floor L and Rosen M. Investigating the phenomenon of helplessness in mentally retarded adults. American Journal of Mental Deficiency 79, 565-572 (1975).

7       Fraser W I and Ozois D. 'He sounds the looks sore. Professionals evaluations of the profoundly handicapped persons pain and distress signals - From Fraser WI and Grieve R (eds) Communicating with normal and retarded children. Wright (1981).

8       Glover E and Mesibov G B. An interest centred sensory stimulation programme for severed and profoundly retarded children. Education and training of the mentally retarded 13 (2), 172-176 (1978)

9       Guess D, Benson H, Siegal-Causey E. Concepts and issues related to choice making and autonomy among persons with severe handicaps. Journal of the Association for persons wit h severe handicaps 10 (2) 79-86 (1985).

10      Hulsegge J and Verheul A. Snoezelen. ROMPA, Chesterfield (1987).

11      Iso-Ahola S E, Macneil R D, Sztmaski D J. Social psychological foundations of therapeutic analysis - an attributional analysis in Iso-Ahola S E (ed) Social Psychological perspectives on leisure and recreation (p301-413) Springfield IL, Charles C, Thomas (1980).

12      Kreger K L. Compensatory Environment programming for the severely retarded, behaviourally disturbed. Mental Retardation, August 29-33 (1971).

13      Lambe L and Hogg J. People with profound retardation and multiple handicaps attending schools or social education centres. Final Repot. Piper Hill School, 200 Yew Tree Lane, Manchester, M23 OFF (1987).

14      Lyons M. Unlocking closed doors to play. Australia and New Zealand Journal of Developmental Disabilities 12 229-33 (1986).

15      Mashall C and Rossman G B. Designing qualitative research, Sage, London (1989).

16      Norris D. Profound mental handicap. Costello, Tunbridge Wells (1982).

17      Prosser G. Vibratory reinforcement in the field of mental handicap: a review. Mental Handicap Research 1, 152-66 (1988).

18      Seligman M E P. Helplessness: On depression development and death. San Francisco: Freeman and Company (1975).

19      Solomon P, Kubzonsky P, Leiderman P, Mendelson J, Trumbull R, Wescler D. Sensory Deprivation: A synopsis. Cambridge: Harvard University (1961).

20      Sykess D, Townsend K, Deakin D. Inflatable structures and their use in the education of children with profound handicaps. Mental Handicap Vol 13, 163-165 (1985).

21      Wilcox B, Bellamy G T. The activities catalogue. Brookes, Baltimore.

## Appendix 1

**Name:**         W    F

**Ward:**         **Ashford**

## Abilities/Disabilities

Although **W** has no speech, he is a very effective communicator through vocal sounds, facial expression, eye contact and gestures. He is able to walk in a toppling fashion and also to crawl, being very active if the mood takes him. **W** is popular with most staff and loves to be the centre of attention. He has a charming personality and is known for his sense of fun and mischief. He is very curious and aware of his surroundings - staff feel he needs a lot of stimulation and attention to keep him occupied.

## Particular problems

**W** is prone to bouts of frustration and self injures during these, hitting his head or banging it on the floor, biting his hands and roaring loudly. Staff say it is very difficult to get through to him in these moods - attention and providing a distraction sometimes works, although staffing shortages at ward level adds to the problem as alternative stimulation cannot always be provided for **W**.

## Mood indicators

**Happy** - **W** smiles, laughs, roars playfully, copies staff's gestures or noises, holds eye contact and co-operates. He reaches out or watches staff/stimuli closely and also seems to amuse himself with his own body movements eg: clapping hands, waving feed. He will clasp staff's hands, accept a cuddle. When really amused he covers his face with his hands and rolls over laughing.

**Sad** - **W** has a sad face with is self explanatory.

**Relaxed** - Quietens down, keeps still, leans in to staff and half closes eyes.

**Agitated** - Stares straight ahead (often out of a window), roars loudly and repeatedly ignores staff/stimuli. Face turns dark. May self injure, hitting head with hand, biting hand or squatting to bang head on floor.

**Interested** - Cues for happy. May sit gazing at person/stimuli intently, reach out to touch or walk/crawl off to explore environment.

**Special relationships** - Shaz (Snoezelen) and Roy (Ward).

**Other information** - **W** particularly enjoys rough and tumble play, noise and visual stimulation - windows and lights fascinate him. Staff feel there is a lot in Snoezelen to interest him and hope the opportunity for regular stimulation, attention and active exploration (eg throwing himself about in the adventure room!) will allow him to vent his frustration in a harmless and enjoyable way.

# Appendix 2

## SNOEZELEN DIARY CARD

| Name | D    B | Date of Session  23 May 1990 |
|------|--------|------------------------------|
| Enabler | Shaz | Type of Session  1 to 1 |

Rooms

| Emotional state/<br>behaviour | Touch | White | Sound | Jacuzzi | Adventure | Sitting |
|---|---|---|---|---|---|---|
| **Tick -** |  |  |  |  |  |  |
| Happy |  |  |  |  | X |  |
| Sad |  |  |  |  |  |  |
| Relaxed |  |  |  | X |  |  |
| Agitated |  |  |  |  |  |  |
| Snoezeling |  |  |  |  | X |  |
| Disinterested |  |  |  | 1 hour |  |  |

**DOMINANT MOOD IN SNOEZELEN: Very relaxed**

**ANY OTHER COMMENTS:**

**D** had a go down the slide, he was very excited. We stayed at the bottom of the slide and he was so relaxed, loving and showed so much affection it was marvellous. He went back to the ward quietly and it was a beautiful session.

## *Appendix 3*

### Behavioural/Qualitative Changes from Interview Data

| Individual | On Sessions | On Ward |
|---|---|---|
| J B | More pleasure<br>More interest in environment<br>More able to relax<br>Increased eye contact | Happier in self<br>More excitable<br>Makes more noises |
| D M | More pleasure<br>More interest in environment<br>More able to relax<br>Attention and concentration improved<br>Few instances of agitation | None |
| C C | More pleasure<br>More interest in environment<br>Can relax independently<br>Happier in self<br>More sociable with other residents<br>Some increase independent movement | None |
| W F | More pleasure<br>More interest in environment<br>Able to relax independently<br>More able to express needs<br>Makes choices<br>No SIB<br>Happier in self<br>Few instances of agitation | None |
| P W | More pleasure<br>More interest in environment<br>Makes independent choices | None |
| B S | Makes independent choices | More relaxed in self with negative consequence. Harder to motivate but ward key unsure if Snoezelen or other factors. |

| Individual | On Sessions | On Ward |
|---|---|---|
| G W | More pleasure<br>More interest in environment<br>More able to relax<br>Willingly attends and<br>participates<br>Less disruptive in sessions<br>Improved attention<br>Has 'blossomed' in character | More relaxed in self<br>Less pain in legs<br>Unhappy when returned<br>from sessions |
| T J | More pleasure<br>More interest in environment<br>More able to relax<br>Stays willingly<br>Can be left on own<br>Is calmer and quieter<br>Fewer stereotypies<br>Initiates contact<br>Will sit with other residents | Has moved wards<br>Changes noted are<br>positive eg: less<br>inclined to wander,<br>calmer in self, more<br>sociable with other<br>residents. Ward key<br>feels partly attributable<br>to move and partly to<br>Snoezelen |
| M H | More pleasure<br>More interest in environment<br>More able to relax<br>Greater awareness enabler's<br>friendship<br>No longer fights relaxation<br>Responses greater and swifter<br>Relaxes mentally on arrival<br>Has been 'opened up' by<br>experiences | Stiffer after sessions<br>Seems more aware of<br>unstimulating environment<br>Other comments suggest<br>personality has developed |
| J P | No changes | No changes |

| Individual | On Sessions | On Ward |
|---|---|---|
| D B | More pleasure<br>More interest in environment<br>More able to relax<br>Improved confidence<br>Less withdrawal and introversion<br>Less fearful<br>Character has developed<br>Fewer instances nipping and<br>pinching<br>Less noisy<br>Rocking decreased<br>More relaxed in self<br>Will initiate contact<br>More able to communicate needs | No changes |
| J B | No changes | No changes |
| B C | More pleasure<br>More interest in environment<br>More able to relax<br>Fewer behaviour problems eg:<br>aggression, attention seeking,<br>shouting, swearing, tantrums<br>Calmer in self<br>Happier in self<br>More co-operative<br>More sensitive to staff needs<br>Voice softer | Seems like different<br>person<br>Fewer behaviour problems<br>eg: aggression, attention<br>seeking, shouting,<br>swearing, tantrums.<br>Calmer in self<br>Happier in self<br>Behaviour more socially<br>acceptable<br>On ward holiday<br>More appreciative staff<br>care<br>Voice softer |
| N B | More agitated when collected<br>for and returned after<br>sessions | Calmer and more relaxed<br>in self<br>Less mischievous on ward<br>Does not bang furniture<br>so much<br>No aggression towards<br>staff<br>Seems happier<br>Fewer instances<br>incontinence<br>Improved concentration |

# A SHORT TRAINING PACKAGE FOR CARE STAFF USING SNOEZELEN ENVIRONMENTS WITH PROFOUNDLY AND MULTIPLY DISABLED CLIENTS: DESIGN, IMPLEMENTATION AND EVALUATION

Louise Elandra Haggar

## ABSTRACT

This chapter addresses the issue of training for care staff using Snoezelen environments with profoundly and multiply disabled clients. It describes a study which involved the design, implementation and evaluation of a short training package. The package was carried out with a group of institutional care staff, who were working on wards where Snoezelen facilities were planned. Results of the evaluation suggested that the package was of benefit to some staff, whilst other appeared to possess the skills and knowledge required to use Snoezelen appropriately without training. They also suggested that the facility may be o particular value in improving the frequency of client/carer interaction.

## INTRODUCTION

This chapter considers the issue of training for care staff who are suing Snoezelen facilities with clients for the first time. In view of the approach emphasising the active involvement of carers, the issue is clearly an important one. The chapter describes a study in which training was given to a group of direct care staff who worked in a large institution for adults with a learning difficulty. The study coincided with the development of two small scale Snoezelen environments, which were to be based on wards housing residents with profound and multiple disabilities. Staff from these wards had become interested in the Snoezelen concept as a result of clients using an existing facility within the Occupational Therapy Department. However, they had no direct experience of using Snoezelen environments themselves, and the fact that staff training had not been planned in conjunction with the new facilities was a source of considerable concern. The author agreed to design, implement and evaluate a short training package as part of her M.Sc. research thesis.

The aim of the package was to teach staff how to use the facilities appropriately with clients. Specifically, the package aimed to provide staff with a basic grasp of the Snoezelen concept, and train staff in the 'enabling' approach which is central to the concept.

The evaluative component of the study addressed the issue of whether training constitutes a useful part of Snoezelen development, or whether care staff already possessed the necessary knowledge and skills to use the facilities appropriately. A secondary aim of the study was to explore the use of quantitive measures in Snoezelen evaluation, with a focus on staff behaviour and staff/client interaction within the environment.

## A brief overview of the evaluative literature in teaching and training

Staff training occupies a significant proportion of the work of psychologists and other professionals in Learning Difficulties, with the practice of training care staff in the use of behavioural techniques having become widespread. Research to demonstrate the efficacy of such training has been somewhat sparse (Milne 1984), and methodological issues have presented a particular problems in this area. Whilst an exhaustive review of the evaluative literature falls beyond the scope of this chapter, some of the main criticisms will be briefly outlined with a view to justifying the design of the study described.

### 1    *Participant Satisfaction*

This is the most common evaluative measure of staff training, however, Milne points out it is highly prone to 'social desirability' effect (Milne 1988). There is little evidence to suggest a relationship between satisfaction and learning, with the two being negatively correlated in some instances (Quilittch 1975; Parker and Thomas 1980). Milne argues that satisfaction data can be useful in establishing participants' willingness to engage in training, with such willingness being a necessary prerequisite of effective training (Milne 1989). As Snoezelen is a relatively new concept and 'resistance to change' is a criticism often applied to staff in institutions (eg Cullen 1987), it seemed appropriate to include a satisfaction measure in this study.

### 2    *Staff Attitudes*

Some studies have sought to measure staff attitude change as a function of training, however, there is little evidence to suggest that such measures are reliable indicators of behavioural change after training (Milne 1988; Wahler and Fox 1980; O'Dell et al 1982). Milne suggests attitudinal data may be useful in establishing people's willingness to use a service (eg Lobitz and Johnson 1975). This consideration is particularly important where a costly facility is planned and resourcing for client services is scarce. Accordingly, this study included a broad measure of staff attitude towards the Snoezelen concept (eg positive vs negative), both before and after training, with the aim of establishing how likely staff were to use the new facilities with clients.

## 3    *Staff Knowledge*

In a review of the behavioural literature in training others, Milne concluded that measurement of knowledge can be a useful accompaniment to direct observation of staff behaviour in determining training outcome (Milne 1988). Presumably, a good grasp of the Snoezelen concept would help staff to use the facility appropriately, eg for leisure, sensory stimulation, relaxation and socialisation, as opposed to structured therapeutic activities. It is also useful to consider knowledge prior to training so the package is designed appropriately, and to consider how this may affect staff expectations, which may be unrealistic. A measure of knowledge was therefore included before and after training.

## 4    *Observation of trained behaviour*

One of the main criticisms of training evaluation studies is the frequent failure to demonstrate that the desired changes in staff behaviour have occurred as a result of training (Milne 1988; Woods and Cullen 1983; Hogg and Mittler 1987). Accordingly, a number of more recent studies have included behavioural observation of staff as an outcome measure (eg Milne 1985; Jones et al 1987), to establish whether or not new skills are being used. This practice is relatively straight forward when observing the well defined skills inherent to behaviour modification (eg: Sanson-Fisher et al 1976) or the implementation of a new ward activity programme (eg: Jones et al 1987), with a number of reliable instruments and techniques being available (eg: The Attendant Behaviour Checklist, Gardner and Giampa 1971).

One of the problems inherent to the evaluation of Snoezelen training is the somewhat nebulous concept of 'enabling' which is central to the concept. 'Enabling' can describe a number of ways of working with people who have a Learning Difficulty, but the Dutch have applied the term specifically to Snoezelen, with staff being known as 'Enablers'. Within this context 'enabling' is described as "a sensitive, caring, non directive approach, in which an atmosphere of safety and security is created and free choice encouraged" (Haggar and Hutchinson 1991). Whilst an observer may hold subjective views about staff ability to 'enable', it is somewhat difficult to measure objectively. For the purpose of this study, a more operational definition of what should go on in the Snoezelen environment was considered, which focused on the interpersonal domain, and also on the provision of sensory stimulation. This definition was adapted from the views of the Dutch (eg: Hulsegge and Verheul 1986), and from a series of 'brainstorming' exercises with experienced Snoezelen workers. It is summarised as follows:

'Enabling' involved the carer engaging in warm interaction with the client, and using the Snoezelen environment to provide the client with a range of pleasant sensory stimulation. Choice and exploration should be encouraged, and the environment used in such a way as to minimise client disability; eg: 'enablers' should help clients move around if they wish to, where mobility is limited. The role of the 'enabler' is to make the experience of Snoezelen a pleasant and rewarding one for clients'.

In order to evaluate the effect of training on staff 'enabling' skills, two well established time sampling methods were used in this study to collect observations of staff behaviour within the Snoezelen environment, before and after training. Such methods had not been used in conjunction with the Snoezelen environment prior to this study, and some adaptation was necessary in order to encompass the special features of the environment; eg: the provision of sensory stimulation. In addition to measuring training outcome, the inclusion of behavioural measures was a useful exercise in attempting to quantify 'enabling' skills, and 'what goes on' within the Snoezelen environment.

## 5    _Time spent with individual clients_

According to Cullen, there is little evidence that training procedures change staff behaviour to the advantage of people with a Learning Difficulty (Cullen 1988). Whilst this conclusion has been disputed (see Milne 1988, for review of studies) and some of the work mentioned in the preceding section suggests otherwise, Cullen draws attention to a point which is often overlooked. He argues that direct, individual contact between care staff ad clients occurs so infrequently, newly training staff behaviour is unlikely to have any effect on clients' lives. Arranging more frequent contact is a necessary precursor for positive change to occur, this "staff training must go hand in hand with other changes if the results are to be worthwhile" (Cullen 1988).

In the case of institutional settings for profoundly and multiply disabled clients, the rate of client/carer interaction has been found to be particularly low (eg: Harmatz 1973; Daily et al 1974: Wright et al 1974: Paton an Stirling 1978). There is no reason to assume that Snoezelen training alone would change this situation, regardless of how much any intervention stressed the importance of individual attention. However, if training goes "hand in hand" with the development of a ward based Snoezelen facility, this combination is arguably powerful for several reasons. Firstly, the environment gives staff the opportunity to exercise newly trained skills. Secondly, the facility alters physical aspects of the ward ecology, by providing a pleasant setting for staff/client interaction. Thirdly, Snoezelen places great emphasis on providing clients with an enjoyable experience, through the provision of individual attention and sensory stimulation. Thus, an hour spent in Snoezelen should provide the client with substantially more contact with the carer than an hour spent on the ward. Training should therefore increase the amount of direct client/carer contact within the Snoezelen environment, by providing staff with a knowledge and skill base which enables them to use the facility appropriately. Whilst it fell beyond the scope of this study to explore these speculations in depth, measures of the frequency and nature of staff/client interaction with the Snoezelen environment were included as part of the training evaluation.

## 6    *Generalisation, Ward Ecology and the Client's Perspective*

As Cullen points out, staff training should have a demonstrably positive effect on the lives of people with a Learning Difficulty (Cullen 1988). Various studies have inferred such an effect by collecting observational data which focused on the desired outcome of staff applying newly training skills in behaviour modification; for example, a reduced frequency of adaptive behaviours (eg: Greene et al 1978; Jones et al 1987). Others have investigated the wide effects of training, by observing staff behaviour in different situations, and establishing whether change is situation specific or more generalised (eg: Milne 1985; Parsons et al 1987). The latter can be useful when considering whether or not such change is desirable from the client's perspective. Whilst some instances of positive generalisation have been demonstrated, eg: an increase in appropriate staff/clients interaction (Paul and Lentz 1977), Milne reported a more negative effect amongst psychiatric nurses after training in behavioural techniques (Milne 1985). In this study, training was associated with less frequent or appropriate interactions with patients during periods of unstructured ward activity, and new skills were used as a means of gaining patient control.

Milne's study illustrates the way in which unintended 'side effects' may arise, following intervention into some aspect of a complex system such as a ward (Willems 1974). The growing interest in behavioural ecology has led to calls for an emphasis on more 'ecological' approaches to training evaluation (eg: Landesman-Dweyer and Knowles 1987), and such an approach seems particularly appropriate in the case of Snoezelen training. If staff are trained to use a facility which is reputed to enhance the client/carer relationship, such an enhancement should be demonstrably beyond the Snoezelen environment. The introduction of a high quality facility is also likely to alter the ward 'ecology' with studies demonstrating a positive impact when the physical settings with a ward are made more pleasant (eg: Jones et al 1983; Rojahn et al 1980; Meinhold and Mulick 1990). In addition, the 'atmosphere' of a ward as a therapeutic milieu has been considered, and Moos has developed a scale which permits quantification of this variable (Ward Atmosphere Scale, Moos 1974). This has been used to demonstrate the benefits of improving ward atmosphere to both patients and staff; eg improved treatment efficacy

53

and reduced re-admission rates (Moos 1976), and to evaluate the implementation of change (eg: Milne 1985).

Regrettably, the time constraints and organisational difficulties inherent to this particular study thwarted the author's attempts to evaluate the wider ranging effects of both training and the Snoezelen facility, in terms of improved life quality for clients. Whilst such an improvement is difficult to measure directly, it could be inferred from changes in staff behaviour occurring beyond the Snoezelen environment (eg: an increase in levels of staff/client interaction on the ward; generalisation of 'enabling' skills beyond Snoezelen, with staff using skills to turn routine activities such as bathtime into a pleasant sensory experience for clients; etc), and from changes in ward atmosphere. The measures considered will be briefly mentioned, as they may be of value in future studies of this nature. They included adapting the W.A.S. (Moos 1974) for use with staff working with a profoundly disabled client group, and observation of staff/client interactions on the ward before and after Snoezelen installation. The latter could be taken during periods of routine contact or unstructured ward activity.

## 7     *Follow up measures*

The lack of follow up data provided in evaluative studies of staff training has been a frequent criticism. Cullen stresses its importance, arguing that many of the positive consequences of training, such as improvement of staff morale, are not maintained over time (Cullen 1988), and Milne recommends the use of longitudinal research designs (Milne 1988). In view of the limited time available to conduct this study, the latter was not an option. However, some follow up data was collected, with the 'novelty effect' anticipated with a new facility such as Snoezelen particularly in mind  This data was qualitative in nature, and took the form of a short structure interview with staff.

## 8     *Baseline Measures*

In an specific evaluation, it is important to establish a baseline before intervention effects can be inferred. Whilst this may seem an obvious point, Milne notes that it is often overlooked in staff training evaluation (Milne 1988). Accordingly, this study included baseline measures of staff behaviour within a Snoezelen environment and staff knowledge about the concept, which were repeated after training.

## 9     *Training Methods - The Independent Variable*

The final consideration in this section is the lack of attention paid to scientific analysis of the actual training methods, which is much lamented by Milne and others (Milne 1988;

Anderson 1987; Parsons et al 1987). Vague descriptions of training programmes are clearly unsatisfactory, however, operational definitions have been provided in only a minority of studies (eg: Farrell 1986; Baker 1986). As Milne points out, such definitions provide clarification, and are also of value in "standardising the manipulation of the independent variable and hence promoting systematic replication, the hallmark of science" (Milne 1988). A detailed description of the package used in this study will therefore be provided, together with a breakdown of time spent in training.

As little attention has been paid to the issue of Snoezelen training. It was important for this study to consider which aspects of the package appeared most effective. The author recorded time spent on each aspect of training (eg: practical sessions, dydactic teaching etc), with care being taken to ensure that all staff received the same 'standardised' package. Video taping the training for subsequent analysis and independent rating of training by outside observers was also considered. However, practical difficulties (eg: availability of personnel to observe) and the possible effects of the former on staff willingness to attend for training resulted in such measures being abandoned.

# DESIGN AND IMPLEMENTATION OF THE TRAINING PACKAGE

## Needs Assessment and Arrangements with Ward Staff

Before designing the training package, a brief needs assessment was conducted. This took the form of discussion with the charge nurses from the two wards involved, who were asked to consult with staff members about their training needs then feed back findings to the author. An item from the questionnaire which constituted part of the training evaluation was also used (see Methodology section for description). Staff needs for training were reported as follows:

1   A brief overview of the Snoezelen concept, preferably without undue reference to complex psychological models or presentation of academic material.

2   A predominantly skills based approach to training, with emphasis on the practical aspects of using Snoezelen environments.

Ward staff were invited to attend for training on a voluntary basis. The majority were care assistants without formal nursing qualifications, who had not participated in previous training events. The charge nurses reported that staff were somewhat nervous about training, and had expressed a strong preference against using techniques such as role play. Whilst the author's experience of using role play in Snoezelen training had been positive, this preference was respected.

Prior to training, the author made informal visits to both wards to meet staff and residents. These visits were intended to familiarise staff with the author, and provide a reassuring function.

## The Design of the Training Package

In order to minimise the practical difficulties of arranging cover for shifts during training, the intervention was kept relatively brief. The package was split into three separate 'blocks', one of which took place in the O.T. Department, the other two taking place on the wards. It was necessary to repeat these 'blocks' several times to accommodate staff from different shifts. This was time consuming and required a considerable amount of organisation, reflecting the need for outside trainers to address these issues when undertaking work within large institutions.

Drawing on the teaching and training literature, the package utilises symbolic (chalk and talk) and iconio (video, handouts) material to set the scene for enactive (partial experience) learning. A number of studies have found practical training to be more effective in producing desired outcome that the more traditional, didactic methods (Milne 1988), and this sequencing is recommended by Farrell (1986).

The package also attempts to encompass features of 'intermediate technology', which Cullen has argued are relevant to staff training (Cullen 1988). These features included:

1    Cost - the package was relatively cheap in terms of nurse and 'expert' time

2    Flexibility - the package was designed for flexible implementation; eg: different 'blocks' could be held in different locations, with minimum disruption to shifts.

3    Substantiality - the package could easily be applied by other staff once the outside trainer had been withdrawn.

A full description of the training package, including content of each 'block' and materials used in presentation, is included in the Methodology section.

## Implementation of Training and Evaluation

Training was planned to coincide with the installation of Snoezelen facilities on the two wards. However, the equipment was not installed as planned, due to various problems with preparing the allocated rooms, eg: heating and satisfaction of fire regulations. At the time of writing up this study, these problems had not been resolved satisfactorily, and the equipment had still not be installed. Both practical aspects of training and behavioural observations had been planned to take place within the new ward based Snoezelen facilities.

These still went ahead, with a compensatory measure of borrowing equipment from the O.T facility, and creating makeshift Snoezelen environments in the allocated rooms on the wards. The author was able to implement the package as planned, however, various organisational difficulties resulted in training taking place somewhat later than planned, which restricted the collection of follow up data for evaluative purposes. Such problems are not uncommon when avaluative work is attempted in an institutional setting, and it is important that the reader is made aware of them, in order to convey something of the process involved in this study. Whilst frustrating for the author, resolving the difficulties and 'salvaging' the study highlighted the need for a flexible research design in this type of evaluative work.

## EVALUATION OF THE TRAINING PACKAGE : METHODOLOGY

### Participants

Participants consisted of 14 care staff, based on the two wards where Snoezelen facilities were planned. The group comprised of 2 charge nurses, 3 qualified nurses, and 9 nursing assistants without formal qualifications. Their mean age was 34 years, 85% were female, and they had worked in institutions for people with a learning difficulty for a mean period of 9 years. The wards they worked on housed a mean of 18 residents, most of whom had profound and multiple disabilities, and many of whom presented with challenging behaviours (eg: self injury, stereotypies). During this study, the ratio of care staff to residents averaged 3:18 (day shifts). Whilst some of the residents had used the O.T. Snoezelen facility, ward staff had little experience of using Snoezelen environments with them. Training was offered on a voluntary basis, with those who attended representing 75% and 41% of total staff from the two wards respectively. Remaining staff chose not to participate, or were unable to do so because of shifts (eg: night staff). 92% of participating staff normally worked one of two day shifts.

### The Training Package

### *Block 1 - Familiarisation with the Snoezelen Environment*

This was a practical session which took place on the ward, using the rooms which had been allocated for the new Snoezelen facilities. Equipment from the O.T. facility was borrowed, and used to create a makeshift Snoezelen environment. Whilst somewhat basic, the facility included features of the typical Snoezelen environment, with 'high tech' equipment being supplemented by home made 'extras'.

For full description and illustration, the interested reader should consult Hulsegge and Verheul (1986), Haggar and Hutchinson (1991), or Rompa U.K. catalogues.

The equipment/extras used in this 'block' were as follows:

*       solar projector and selection of 'effect' wheels, which were used to
        transmit changing patterns of colour onto walls and ceilings. Windows
        in the room were blacked out for maximum effect.

\*       Cassette recorder and a selection of 'New Age' music. This is used in Snoezelen environments, relaxation, meditation, etc.

\*       Hand held fibre optic spray, with automatic colour change.

\*       Scented candles, joss sticks, and a selection of aromatherapy massage oils for tactile/olfactory stimulation.

\*       Cushions and soft bean bags.

\*       'Feelie Box' containing a variety of items for tactile stimulation which O.T. staff had accumulated, eg: loofah, fur, shaving brushes, etc.

Staff were invited to spend up to an hour 'trying out' the environment with residents, whilst the author observed non intrusively. They were encouraged to identify any specific difficulties arising, so these could be commented on in Block 2 of the training, and to share positive experiences. Feedback on performance was given at the end of the session.

Behavioural observations were taken during the sessions. The author also attempted to put staff at ease, by chatting informally with staff about the planned facility and her own experience of Snoezelen. As participation in training was entirely voluntary, it was vital to gain staff confidence and co-operation at an early stage. Five 'familiarisation' sessions were held in total, to accommodate staff from different shifts, with each one lasting three hours.

## Block 2 -      An Introduction to the Snoezelen Concept

This session involved a combination of didactive and experimental teaching, using iconic materials and the O.T. Snoezelen facility. It was held in the O.T. Department.

### Plan of Session

Video (15 minutes)

Introduction to the Snoezelen concept - a 'talk' accompanied by slides and handout (1 hour)

Discussion and questions (30 minutes allowed - time varied with different staff groups)

Coffee break (30 minutes)

The Snoezelen Experience - Practical (1 hour)

## Iconic Materials

These comprised of a short video, slides to accompany the didactic teaching and a handout which staff kept. The video was made at Whittington Hall Hospital and showed activities within the large scale Snoezelen facility which is based there. Development of the facility was also described with a number of different staff giving their views and describing their experience of Snoezelen. The slides were also borrowed from the hospital and were used to accompany the 'talk'. Staff were given a handout which summarised the material covered for the purpose of future reference.

## The O.T. Snoezelen Facility

This contained all equipment and 'extras' described in the previous section, together with a fixed 6ft 'bubble tube' with automatic colour change (similar in appearance to the once popular glycerine lamp!). The equipment had been arranged beneath a large, brightly coloured canopy which blocks out light and creates an enclosed and private space. The flooring comprised of the soft, plastic covered blocks which are found in 'soft play' environments with additional bean bags, cushions and an air filled mattress.

## The 'Talk'

The aim of this was to provide staff with an understanding of the Snoezelen concept. This history and development of Snoezelen were summarised together with key principles of the approach, eg: leisure, sensory stimulation, relaxation. The 'enabling' approach was discussed in detail and findings from the Whittington Hall evaluation were briefly summarised. "Do It Yourself" Snoezelen was as described (eg: using homemade Snoezelen equipment where resourcing is scarce), together with ways in which the approach can be extended beyond the Snoezelen environment (eg: making bathtime a pleasant sensory experience for clients). The author concluded by sharing some of her own experiences of Snoezelen, describing several former clients who had found the approach of value. In terms of disability and specific difficulties, these clients were comparable to residents from the two wards involved.

## Discussion and Questions

Staff were invited to discuss material presented together with issues arising from 'familiarisation' session and to raise questions.

## The Snoezelen 'Experience'

The aim of this was to provide staff with a Snoezelen 'experience' and to consider ways in which the environment/equipment might be used for particular clients' enjoyment. Staff spent 30 minutes relaxing in the environment. The remaining 30 minutes were spent exploring the ways in which different pieces of equipment could be used to provide different sensations (eg: bubble tube for visual, vibrotactile stimulation).

## *Block 3 - Enactive/Practical Session*

The aim of this session was to provide staff with an environment in which new knowledge and skills could be practised 'live' with clients. A makeshift Snoezelen environment was created on the ward, as in Block 1. Each staff member spent one hour in the environment with a client whilst the author observed non intrusively. (In some cases, there was client 'change over' during the hour as the amount of time some wished to spend in the environment was less than an hour. No client was forced to remain against his or her will). Behavioural observations were taken during this session and feedback on performance was given to each staff member at the end of each hour. Six of these sessions were held in total, to accommodate staff from different shifts, with each one lasting three hours.

## Notes on Design of Package

This package was designed specifically for care staff with the practical sessions being planned in such away as to facilitate the collection of behavioural observations. Whilst somewhat time consuming, the involvement of more than one training or access to a larger Snoezelen facility would considerably reduce time spent in training. There is scope to vary the content of material presented, for example, a more academic presentation with possible theoretical models underlying Snoezelen could be made in accordance with the needs of different staff groups. Additional material could also be included in the practical sessions, eg: role play, 'live modelling with clients, etc.

## **Measures**

### 1    Staff Knowledge About/Attitudes Towards the Snoezelen Concept

A short 'ad hoc' questionnaire was designed to elicit staff knowledge about Snoezelen and to broadly ascertain staff attitude towards the concept, eg: positive vs negative (see

Appendix 1 for sample item). The questionnaire comprised 78 items, 5 of which were used to measure knowledge. These items were derived from the author's own knowledge of the Snoezelen concept with material for correct responses being included in the training package. Questions were open ended with a view to establishing how much staff knew without the 'prompting' provided by multiple choice designs. They covered the fundamental principles of the Snoezelen concept (eg: leisure, sensory stimulation, relaxation and the provision of individual attention); the type of equipment/extras staff would expect to find in a typical environment; ideas for D.I.Y. Snoezelen (eg: 'homemade' alternatives to equipment where resourcing is scarce) and 'creative' use of Snoezelen equipment (eg: using an item of equipment to stimulate more than one sense).

Of the remaining 3 items, 2 were used to ascertain staff attitudes with 1 yielding qualitative data within this domain, eg; why staff held a particular attitude towards Snoezelen. The remaining item was used as part of the needs assessment in the pre training format and as a feedback item in the post training format. Staff were asked to complete the questionnaire before participating in training then again afterwards. All responses were kept anonymous, in an effort to allay staff anxieties that the questionnaire constituted an 'examination'.

2    Staff 'Enabling' Skills Within the Snoezelen Environment

This measure involved the collection of behavioural observations within the 'makeshift' Snoezelen environments created on the wards using two time sampling methods. The first was the Attendant Behaviour Checklist (A.B.C.L. Gardner and Giampa 1971) which has been used to evaluate training outcome in a number of studies (eg: Milne 1985; Cullen 1986). The A.B.C.L. allows the observer to assign staff behaviour to one of twelve categories. Categories 1-6 encompass the type of behaviour one might expect to occur within the Snoezelen environment with some being expected to increase or decrease in frequency after training. These categories were, 'Supervision', 'Personal Care', 'Socialisation', 'Punishment', 'Training' and 'Rejection' plus an additional 'Other Activities' for behaviours which were impossible to classify. The remaining categories were not considered relevant to Snoezelen (eg: record keeping and ward management categories) and were therefore excluded. It was also necessary to include additional behaviours in the existing categories in order to encompass the features of the Snoezelen environment. Accordingly, 'provision of sensory stimulation' was included in the 'Socialisation' category, and 'showing client how to use equipment' was included in the 'Training' category. A full description of each category together with adaptations made for the purpose of this study, have been included in Appendix 2. Training staff to 'enable' should result in an increase in 'Socialisation' and 'Training' behaviours (eg: interacting warmly with clients, showing them how to use Snoezelen equipment) and a corresponding reduction in rejecting and punishing behaviours.

The Social Reinforcement Rating Scale (S.R.R.S. Gelfand et al 1967) was also used as an outcome measure. The S.R.R.S. focuses on the consequences of a given interaction (eg: reward, punishment, ignored) whether these consequences are appropriate or inappropriate and who gave the consequences (eg: staff or client). Rearding, reciprocal interaction is fundamental to Snoezelen, therefore training should work to facilitate this. This measure also considered the number of times clients gave appropriate rewards to carers within the Snoezelen environment and how frequently they punished or ignored carer attempts to interact with them. If a high frequency of the latter two consequences was recorded this would suggest that clients are unrewarding or aversive to carers and the frequency of carer attempts to interact with them in Snoezelen would be expected to decrease over time.

Observation Procedure

All observations were carried out by the author, within the 'makeshift' Snoezelen environments. Staff were told that the author was observing client response to Snoezelen for a related project. Observations were made during Blocks 1 and 3 of the training (Familiarisation and Practical sessions) with the former representing a baseline measure of 'enabling' skills and the latter constituting a post training measure. The A.B.C.L. was based on a 10 second sample of each staff members' behaviour recorded at 30 second intervals. The S.R.R.S. data were recorded instantaneously using the same sheet. Observation was split into three 10 minute periods during the hour, eg: 10 minutes on, 10 minutes off. This allowed behaviour to be sampled throughout a 1 hour period and resulted in a total of 30 minutes pre training and 30 minutes post training observation.

Total time spent in 'familiarisation' sessions was 15 hours, of which 7.5 were observed (pre training measure). Total time spent in 'practical' sessions was 18 hours, of which 9 were observed (post training measure). The 3 hours discrepancy is accounted for by an additional 'practical' block which was held to accommodate shifts.

Observer Reliability and Observee Reactivity

A major problem with this study was the lack of available personnel to assist with collection of data which resulted in all observations being made by the author. A reliability check was carried out with the assistance of the field supervisor, a clinical psychologist who had extensive experience of behavioural observation. He and the author rated staff behaviour in video recording of a series of roleplays for the duration of 1 hour using the A.B.C.L. and S.R.R.S. The recordings had been made for the purpose of staff training and included samples of appropriate and inappropriate interactions with clients. Whilst it would have been preferable to video staff/client interactions within the Snoezelen environment, attempts to do this met with strong resistance from staff. A second option of using experienced Snoezelen workers to role play 'good' and 'bad' examples of practice was considered but this was not practically viable.

The issue of observe reactivity was also considered with staff attempting to 'impress the trainer' being a possibility. Such an attempt would be expected to decrease over time, therefore reactivity was investigated by comparing the first and last ten minutes of observations within each given period.

## 3    Staff Satisfaction with Training

This was established by means of an 8 item Satisfaction Questionnaire which staff were asked to complete after training (see Appendix 3 for sample item). The questionnaire was a variation of one which has been used extensively in service evaluation by Northumberland District Health Authority. Items were rated on a scale of 1-4 and included quality of training, recommendation of package to other staff and overall satisfaction with training. Completed sheets were kept anonymous, in an effort to reduce 'socially desirable' responses.

## 4    Follow Up to Training Intervention, using Structured Interview with Staff

The author had planned to collect follow up data by repeating behavioural observations within the new Snoezelen facilities over a period of time. However, in view of the difficulties outlined, these plans were abandoned in favour of collecting qualitative follow up data using a short structured interview with staff. The Whittington Hall Project (N.D.H.A. 1991) involved extensive use of structured interviews and 6 of the items which had been found to yield the most valuable data were included. Specifically, these items sought to identify sources of job satisfaction and frustration for care staff, to establish the perceived effect of the Snoezelen facility on these sources and to give an idea of client response within the 'makeshift' facilities which were created for the purpose of training (see Appendix 4 for sample item). The interview also sought to establish whether the delay in installation had resulted in a negative effect on staff enthusiasm for the concept. (Data from the 'Knowledge and Attitude' and 'Satisfaction' questionnaire had indicated a high level of enthusiasm after training).

## Interview Procedure and Subjects

Interviews were carried out 6 weeks after training. Limited time available at this late stage of the study resulted in only a small sample of staff being interviewed. Six were interviewed in total with the group comprising of a charge nurse, trained nurse and nursing assistant from the two respective wards. An attempt to reduce sample bias was made by selecting the latter 4 staff from 2 different shifts. Interviews were carried out by the author and took place on the wards with each lasting approximately 20 minutes. They were conducted in a relaxed and friendly manner. Subjects were assured anonymity with a view to reducing 'socially desirable' responses.


# RESULTS

## The Training Package

Total time spent in training was recorded by the author together with time spent on each individual component (eg: video, didactic teaching etc). The results are given in Figure 1 and Figure 2. Figure 1 depicts the proportion of total time spent on each component. From a total of 42.75 training hours, 82.25% of time was spent in practical sessions (eg: familiarisation, experimental and enactive)..

The total number of hours spent in practical sessions could have been reduced considerably had more than one training or large scale Snoezelen facility been available.

Figure 2 depicts the total amount of training received by each individual staff member and the way in which this was split. As can be seen, the intervention was relatively brief with each person spending 5.25 hours in training, less a 30 minute coffee break. (Breaks have been included in Figures 1 and 2 as the author was available throughout these periods for informal questions and private consultation). Whilst 'Blocks 1, 2 and 3 were repeated to accommodate staff from different shifts, each staff member received the same standardised package and spent the same amount of time in training.

*FIGURE 1*

Breakdown of total hours spent in training

| | |
|---|---|
| 0.75 | Video |
| 3.00 | Didactic |
| 15.0 | Familiariazation |
| 18.0 | Enactive |
| 3.00 | Experimental |
| 1.50 | Questions/Discussion |
| 1.50 | Breaks |

Total time: 42.75
84.25% of total time was spent on practicals

*FIGURE 2*

Breakdown of training hours given to each individual

| | |
|---|---|
| 0.25 | Video |
| 1.00 | Didactic |
| 1.00 | Familiarization |
| 1.00 | Enactive |
| 1.00 | Experimental |
| 0.50 | Questions/Discussion |
| 0.50 | Breaks |

Total hours training 5.25

## The Training Package (continued)

Quality of training was not rated by independent observers, as no personnel were available to be this. However, informal feedback from the two charge nurses and O.T. staff working in the wards was positive. The section on 'satisfaction' data deals with participating ratings.

The independent variable in this study was therefore a brief training intervention which was predominantly 'skills based' and received positive feedback from staff. Findings described in the following sections suggest this type of intervention can be effective in training care staff how to use Snoezelen environments appropriately with clients with the didactic and experimental aspects of teaching working to improve knowledge about the concept.

## Questionnaire Data

### Response Rate

Questionnaire response rate was 100%, although this involved considerable 'chasing up' on the part of the author! Not all staff could be persuaded to complete questionnaires directly before and after 'Blocks' 1 and 3 of training, therefore late responders could well have consulted with colleagues about 'knowledge' items. 85% of staff completed the first questionnaire on time with the figure dropping to 64% for the second.

### Staff Knowledge about Snoezelen

Date from 'knowledge' items are summarised below in Table 2 with numbers of staff answering items correctly expressed as percentages.

*Table 2: Staff Knowledge about Snoezelen*

| Questionnaire Items | % of Staff answering Correctly (n=14) | |
|---|---|---|
| | Before Training | After Training |
| Sensory Stimulation | 85 | 100 |
| Leisure | 50 | 85 |
| Relaxation | 100 | 100 |

## Reliability and Reactivity Checks

A test of reliability of the author's observations was carried out (see Methodology section for test description. Inter rater reliability between the author and field supervisor was found to be 88.2% (120 observations), thus it was concluded that the author's observations were reliable. Observe reactivity was tested by comparing observations from the first and last 10 minutes of every observation period for each staff member. No significant bias emerged, therefore a low rate of reactivity was inferred.

*Table 3: Mean Per Cent Frequency of Categories of the Attendant Behaviour Checklist (A.B.C.L.)*

| Staff Behaviour Category | Mean % Frequency | | | |
| | Before Training | | After Training | |
| | Mean | S.D. | Mean | S.D. |
|---|---|---|---|---|
| (1) Supervision | 7.64 | 3.15 | 6.57 | 3.51 |
| (2) Personal care | 1.5 | 1.72 | 1.28 | 1.66 |
| (3) Socialisation | 23.42 | 11.22 | 32.42* | 5.51 |
| (4) Punishment | 0.42 | 0.90 | 0.21 | 0.55 |
| (5) Training | 9.07 | 6.36 | 12.07~ | 3.23 |
| (6) Rejection | 11.71 | 15.64 | 2.28* | 4.75 |
| (7) Other Activity | 6.28 | 5.48 | 5.07 | 3.61 |

* $p < 0.001$ (n=14, Total observations 1680, 840 before training and 840 after training)    ~ $p < 0.005$

## Total Number of Observations Collected

A total of 840 pre training and 840 post training observations were collected of staff behaviour within the 'makeshift' Snoezelen environments, eg: 60 pre and 60 post observations for each of the 14 staff. Each one was coded using the A.B.C.L. and S.R.R.S. All observations were collected between 1.00pm and 4.00pm with Familiarisation and Enactive training 'blocks' being held during this afternoon period.

*Table 4: Percentage of Staff having Knowledge about Snoezelen*

| Knowledge Category | Before Training | After Training |
|---|---|---|
| Individual Attention | 85 | 100 |
| From Holland | 64 | 100 |
| Named > 2 Items Equipment | 92 | 100 |
| 'Creative' Use Equipment | 35 | 78 |
| Had > 2 Ideas 'D.I.Y.' Snoezelen | 28 | 85 |

## Staff Knowledge about Snoezelen (continued)

As can be seen, staff appeared to have a good baseline knowledge of Snoezelen. This was particularly true of the two charge nurses who had instigated the development of the facilities, with the author noting this from informal discussions prior to training. High baseline knowledge may well have been a function of prior enlighten might from charge nurses, or discussion with O.T. staff and visits to the O.T. facility. Staff knowledge improved after training and the improvement was statistically significant ($p>0.001$ Wilcoxon test: $t = 0$, $d.f. = 12$). However, part of this improvement may have arisen from 'late' questionnaire returners consulting with colleagues. A particular improvement was found in responses to items tapping 'creative use of equipment (eg: stimulation of more than one sense), and ideas for 'D.I.Y.' Snoezelen, both of which were covered in the didactic and experimental components of training. This knowledge is arguably useful, firstly for the client to gain maximum benefit from the Snoezelen environment and secondary where resourcing is scarce.

In relationships to the independent variable, material for correct response to questionnaire items was covered mainly by 'Block 2' of the training package (ie: didactic, iconic and experimental components of training). It was therefore inferred that improvement in knowledge was a function of these components of training.

Staff Attitude Towards Snoezelen

Eighty five per cent of staff held a broadly positive attitude towards Snoezelen (eg: they thought it was a "good thing for profoundly and multiply disabled people") before training, with the remaining 15% responding with "not sure". All staff held a broadly positive attitude after training.

It seemed likely that prior knowledge about the concept had resulted in the formation of these attitudes. Staff were asked to qualify their 'good/bad' statements and responses were not unduly influenced by training. Most frequent responses incorporated staff knowledge about the concept, eg: "Snoezelen allows residents to relax", "allows staff to give individual attention", "provides stimulation" etc.

A.B.C.L. Data

The most striking feature of the A.B.C.L. data where the high frequency of staff 'Socialization' behaviours observed within the Snoezelen environment, both before and after training. Whilst comparative frequency data were not collected on the wards, the literature on client/carer interactions within institutional settings suggest such rates would have been highly unlikely during a typical afternoon period.

'Socialization' behaviours were found to increase in frequency after training by 10% and this finding was statistically significant (p<0.001, Wilcoxon test: t = 3, d.f. = 13). There was a corresponding reduction in 'Rejection'. which was also statistically significant (p<0.001, Wilcoxon test: t = 3, d.f. = 9). However, this finding was mostly attributable to the behaviour of three particular staff members. Their pre training behaviour was characterised by a high frequency of 'Rejection' and low frequency of 'Socialization' behaviours, with this trend reversing dramatically after training. The majority of remaining staff had shown high frequencies of 'Socialization' and low frequences of 'Rejection' before training, with a slight increase in frequency of the former after training.

'Training' behaviours increased after training (eg: showing client how to use equipment) with the increase being statistically significant (p<0.05, Wilcoxon test: t = 15, d.f. = 14). However, this trend was again attributable to the behaviour of the same three staff members with remaining staff showing high frequencies of 'Training' behaviours before training and a slight increase afterwards. There was little change in frequencies of behaviours from the remaining A.B.C.L. categories with 'Punishment' being universally low.

From these findings, it was concluded that the training intervention increased the frequency of 'Socialization' and 'Training' behaviours and reduced the frequency of 'Rejection' within the Snoezelen environment, with increase and reduction being particularly marked in three staff members. In relation to the independent variable, it was inferred that this change was a function of the experimental aspects of 'Block' 2 and all of 'Block' 3, (enactive/practical session), which covered 'enabling' skills.

### Data from the Social Reinforcement Rating Scales (S.R.R.S.)

S.R.R.S. data are summarised in Table 4 below (mean frequencies)

*Table 4: Summary of Social Reinforcement Rating Scale (S.R.R.S.) Data, Indicating Interaction Frequencies and Categories*

| Consequence Provided To Staff by Client | Reward Appro | Punish Inapp | Ignore Appro | Ignore Inapp | Ignore Appr | Ignore Inapp |
|---|---|---|---|---|---|---|
| **A) Before Training** | | | | | | |
| Mean % Frequency | 24.57 | - | 2.5 | - | 5.0 | |
| S.D. | 18.33 | - | - | 4.79 | - | 6.73 |

Uncoded: Mean = 9.64, S.D. = 6.73
Total: Mean = 42.07, S.D. = 14.88
Sum of Interactions observed = 589, of which 58.4% were appropriately rewarded by clients

| Consequence Provided To Staff by Client | Reward Appro | Punish Inapp | Ignore Appro | Ignore Inapp | Ignore Appr | Ignore Inapp |
|---|---|---|---|---|---|---|
| **B) After Training** | | | | | | |
| Mean % Frequency | 29.85 | - | 2.92 | - | 4.57 | |
| S.D. | 10.48 | - | - | 5.67 | - | 5.17 |

Uncoded: Mean = 14.07, S.D. = 8.85
Total: Mean = 52.14* S.D. = 6.90
Sum of Interactions observed = 730, of which 57.26 were appropriately rewarded by clients
  *p< 0.001

The S.R.R.S. data were similarly striking, in view of the high frequency of interactions observed both before and after training. Again, whilst comparative data was not collected on the wards, the literature has described a very low frequency of staff/client interaction. Frequency of interactions was found to increase after training and the increase was statistically significant (p<0.001, Wilcoxon test: t = 5, d.f. = 14). However, this increase was mostly attributable to the behaviour of the three staff members described in the preceding section. Consequence of interactions for staff were also recorded, ie: clients' responses to interactions. For the purpose of this study, consequences were defined as follows:

* 'Appropriate Reward': A positive response from clients, eg: smiling, laughing, reaching for Snoezelen equipment offered by staff etc.

* 'Inappropriate Punishment': A negative, punishing response from clients, eg: pushing staff away, screaming, displaying self injurious behaviour etc.

* 'Inappropriate Ignore': Client ignores staff attempt at interaction.

There was no significant change in interaction consequence after training. It was interesting to note that the number of interactions rewarded appropriately by clients did not increase in correspondence with the higher frequency of interactions observed after training. This suggests that newly trained behaviour had no effect on client responses. However, staff were rewarded appropriately by clients from more than 50% of interactions both before and after training. Considering the severe nature of clients' disabilities, this rate appears quite high. The consequence of 'inappropriate punishment' was given by staff to three particular clients; who were presented with challenging behaviours. These clients appeared to find contact with staff aversive, however, the author noted that staff dealt with this by moving gradually closer to them throughout the 1 hour period in Snoezelen. When individual datasheets for these staff were examined, the 'inappropriate punishment' consequence was found to decrease in frequency over time.

From these findings, it was concluded that frequency of staff/client interaction was increased by training, with this increase being particularly marked in three staff members. In relation to the independent variable, it was inferred that this increase was a function of experimental and enactive components of training, which covered 'enabling' skills (ie: part of 'Block' 2, and all of 'Block' 3). The findings also suggested that the consequences of interaction with clients who presented with challenging behaviour may be punishing to staff, and that appropriate use of the Snoezelen environment may decrease this consequence over time.

## Satisfaction Data

### Response Rate

Of the 14 participants, 92% returned satisfactory questionnaires (n=13).

### Satisfaction Ratings

Staff rated the 8 items on a scale of 1-4 (eg: Excellent, Good, Fair and Poor for quality of training), with scales being reversed for some items. Quality of training was rated as 'Excellent' by 15% of staff with the remaining 85% rating quality as 'Good'. 92% reported that they had received the kind of training that they wanted and that most of their needs had been met by the package. 61% said they would definitely recommend the package to other wards with 76% stating that they would ask for the package again to train new staff. There was a 50/50 split for overall satisfaction ratings, with half of the staff being 'Very Satisfied' and half being 'Mostly Satisfied'. 61% thought the package had helped to use Snoezelen more effectively with residents. No item received a rating of less than 'Fair'. The fact that all 14 staff attended all 3 training 'Blocks' also suggests satisfaction with the package.

### Follow Up Data from Structured Interviews

Six of the 14 participants (3 from each ward) were interviewed by the author at follow up, six weeks after training intervention. Whilst all of these staff expressed disappointment at the delay in installing the Snoezelen facilities, there was no indication that their motivation to use them with clients had waned. Subject responses to certain items had much in common with interview data from the Whittington Hall Project. For example, all 6 subjects gave "insufficient staff to give residents enough attention" as the most frustrating thing about their jobs, and all gave client related sources of job satisfaction, eg: "getting to know the residents", "building relationships with residents", "getting a positive response from residents" etc. All thought the new facilities would influence these factors in a positive way by providing a pleasant, ward based environment which residents would enjoy spending time in and where individual attention could be provided. 60% thought using the Snoezelen facility would help staff to relax as well as clients and reduce stress levels on the ward. 60% also reported new and positive responses amongst clients within the 'makeshift' Snoezelen environments.

Sample of these were as follows:

"**C** gets very frustrated and is usually very noisy on the ward which is annoying for other residents. Snoezelen seemed to have calming effect on him and other residents go some peace and quiet"

"**P** is very tense but I noticed he relaxed in Snoezelen. He also let me sit near him which was very unusually for **P**".

"It hard to find anything at **L** enjoys but she seemed to like the fibre optic and was watching the lights change colour. I've never seen her smile before!"

One of the most important things to emerge from the interview data was the benefits staff perceived in basing the new facilities on the wards. They reported that using the O.T. facility has presented problems in terms of providing staff cover, with the size of the hospital site and ward location also necessitating the arrangement of special transport for residents. This had resulted in only a few residents being able to use the facility on a regular basis and care staff being unable to attend with them. Staff thought a ward based facility would improve this situation by providing 'instant access' and cover would not be a problem (eg: one member of staff covering whilst two used Snoezelen with residents, with all three being available on the ward in the event of an emergency).

<u>'Equipment Borrowing' and Extra Input for Occupational Therapy Staff - A 'Side Effect' of Training</u>

When the interviews were conducted at follow up, a positive 'side effect' of training emerged, which staff reported had arisen from the author's idea of creating 'makeshift' Snoezelen environments on the wards by borrowing equipment from the O.T. facility. After training, the charge nurse from one ward had arranged to borrow this equipment on a regular basis over weekends, to compensate for the delay in installation so as to "keep staff enthusiasm going". A member of O.T. staff had arranged to bring Snoezelen equipment onto the other ward on Monday afternoons providing additional input and the opportunity for staff to use the equipment with residents. Staff from a third ward had also become interested in Snoezelen and the O.T. had made a similar arrangement to bring equipment over on a weekly basis and introduce staff to the concept. These findings appear to reflect continued staff interest in Snoezelen after training with involvement from O.T. staff helping to sustain this and, providing valuable input to other staff.

# DISCUSSION

## Overview of Results

Overall, the results of the evaluation suggested that the Snoezelen training package used in this study was helpful to some staff. Training objectives were met, with staff knowledge about Snoezelen improving, and 'enabling' skills being demonstrated more frequently within the Snoezelen environment after training. Specifically, it was predicted that training would result in an increase in staff/client interaction, an increase in staff 'Socialization' and 'Training' behaviours, and a corresponding reduction in 'Rejection' within Snoezelen. These predictions were confirmed with observed changes being particularly striking in three staff members. Such changes are arguably positive from the client's perspective and suggest the 'enabling' approach is of value to this client group. However, the kind of lasting benefit to clients which Cullen and others have argued should arise from staff training cannot be inferred from the results of this study, as there was insufficient time to establish whether behavioural changes were maintained over time (Cullen 1988; Hogg and Mittler 1986). The majority of staff were found to have a positive attitude towards Snoezelen and a good knowledge of the concept before training, with most being capable 'enablers' prior to training intervention. In the case of this staff group, there appeared to be a relationship between the attitudinal, knowledge and behavioural domains, with training apparently providing an enhancing function to at least two of these. This enhancement was relatively slight for the majority of staff. As questionnaire data was kept anonymous, it was not possible to identify responses from staff who showed the greatest degree of behavioural change after training. In their case, change may have occurred as a function of increased knowledge, skill learning or possibly training serviced to improve confidence or motivation. It is also possible that change was not directly related to training, eg: occurring as a result of pressure from colleagues, desire to impress trainer, etc.

Apart from providing measures of training outcome, the collection of behavioural observations was a useful exercise in the quantification of 'enabling' skills and 'what goes on' between clients and carers with the Snoezelen environment. The study demonstrated that behavioural measures can be used in an evaluative tool within the environments and this had implications for both future research and quality assurance measures for Snoezelen. These will be briefly discussed in the section on 'Wider Implications of the Study'.

The interview data gave a somewhat more positive view of at least some institutional care staff than had been reported in the literature (eg: Daily et al 19784; Dalglesh and Matthews 1981). Subjects interviewed seemed aware of the clients' needs beyond the provision of basic nursing care and expressed a desire to spend more time giving individual attention. They also took pleasure in the new and positive responses reported within the Snoezelen environment. Whilst very limited, these findings do not support the view that care staff find profoundly and multiply disabled clients unrewarding or aversive. This implies that the low rate of client/carer interaction reported in the literature may be a function of factors other than staff actively avoiding contact with clients; eg: low staff/client staffing ratios, physical setting of ward, lack of 'inspiration' for appropriate activities for client groups, etc.

Interview data was also useful in terms of service planning. They suggested that siting Snoezelen facilities on the wards may be preferable to investing in a separate, large scale facility, in terms of easy access and encouraging carer involvement with minimal disruption to shifts.

In an overall sense, the results of the training evaluation suggested that the staff involved had the knowledge, skills and motivation to use their new, ward based Snoezelen facilities appropriately with clients. It was particularly encouraging to see staff adopting the compensatory measure of 'equipment borrowing', in the face of continuing delays to Snoezelen installation. Findings also showed that appropriate use of the Snoezelen environment resulted in high frequencies of staff/client interaction, high frequencies of staff 'Socialization' and 'Training' behaviours, and low frequencies of 'Rejection'. Providing future research demonstrates that these effects are maintained over time, indications are that the Snoezelen environment has potential to improve both life quality for the profoundly disabled client group and, job satisfaction for carers.

Problems with Design of the Study

One of the major weaknesses of this study was the fact that all observations were carried out by the author during practical training 'Blocks'. Whilst every attempt was made to carry out repeated asures outside of the 'Blocks' and to involve other personnel in the ratings, these were thwarted by various organisational problems and the limited time available to conduct both training and evaluation. Time also restricted the collection of follow up data in addition to the interviews, which would have improved the study. Such difficulties are frequently inherent to conducting evaluative work within an institutional setting, with organisational problems usually being beyond the researcher's control. A good example of this was the delay in installing the new Snoezelen facilities which resulted in a large proportion of planned evaluative work having to be abandoned. This was unfortunate, as the inclusion of skill generalisation and 'life quality' measures would have strengthened the study considerably.

The 'knowledge' questionnaires were uniformly unpopular with staff with many believing they constituted an examination. After completing the study, the author's subjective view was that an interview format would have been preferable although this would have involved additional time.

Finally, it is important to note that training in this study was provided on a voluntary basis which resulted in a self selected staff group. All participants worked on wards where Snoezelen facilities were planned, with those volunteering for training arguably having the greatest interest in and enthusiasm for the concept. Such factors are bound to influence training outcome and create a somewhat 'rosy' picture. This picture may well have been different had the group been selected from a wider population of hospital staff with those staff who are most resistant to change providing the greatest challenge to trainers. It is also possible that the two wards differed from others on a number of variables which may be associated with interest in new innovations and the desire to implement change. A more comprehensive study could include 'controls' from wards without plans for facilities, in order to consider such variables.

Wider Implications of the Study

Whilst it was not possible to evaluate the new Snoezelen facilities during the course of this study, the behavioural data collected was arguably of value beyond serving the purpose of a training outcome measure. Firstly, it demonstrated high frequencies of client/carer interactions and staff 'Socialization' behaviours and low rates of 'Rejection' occurring within the Snoezelen environment. In view of the universally low rates of interaction reported on typical institutional wards (eg: Cullen et al 1984), the data was particularly striking. Cullen (1988) pointed out the need to arrange more frequent individual client/carer contact before considering any training objectives. The findings from this study suggest Snoezelen facilities may have a vital role to play in facilitating such contact.

Secondly, the data illustrated that activity within the Snoezelen environment can withstand 'hard' quantitative analysis. Whilst the Dutch would probably scorn such an analysis, the inclusion of a behavioural measure may serve to strengthen future evalutive studies of the environments. New and innovative approaches are frequently criticised for lack of supporting empirical data (eg: Cunningham 1989), with the design of appropriate outcome measures presenting something of a problem. This has been particularly true of Snoezelen, with the approach emphasising leisure rather than measurable, therapeutic outcome. The high frequency of client/carer interaction which was observed in this study suggests it may be useful for future researchers to focus on this rather than concentrating exclusively on client behaviour within the Snoezelen environment.

Attempting to quantify 'enabling' skills may also be useful in the development of quality assurance measures for new and existing Snoezelen facilities. From the client's perspective, it is important to develop such measures in order to monitor activities within Snoezelen and ensure the continuation of good practice once the 'novelty value' has worn off. Furthermore, an operational definition of 'what should go on' in the Snoezelen environment is important in the design of appropriate staff training interventions. There is no reason why such a definition cannot encompass both subjective and objective dimensions of 'enabling' thus retaining the philosophy behind the approach and providing staff with practical guidelines.

In terms of service provision, the interview data suggested that basing Snoezelen facilities on wards is useful in practical terms, particularly where a large hospital site is involved. There are also implications for developing facilities within small group homes for profoundly disabled clients living in the community which can become 'mini institutions' in themselves (eg: Rawlings 1985). Future evaluative research may demonstrate that apart from being cheaper than large scale developments, the small scale Snoezelen facility conveys greater benefit to clients in terms of easy access and involvement of carers. However, the two may not be comparable in terms of qualitative experience from the client's perspective. In terms of leisure activities, a possible parallel for the non disabled person may be the experience of watching a video at home and seeing a film in a large multi-screen cinema complex. Ideally a comprehensive service should provide a choice of leisure facilities for clients and the opportunity to enjoy both types of 'Snoezelen experience'.

Finally, as with any innovation in care practice, there is a very real danger of staff using Snoezelen environments inappropriately with clients. Whilst evidence for this did not emerge during the course of this study, the literature on behaviour modification provides a potent warning of what can go wrong when well intentioned trainers attempt to implement change by teaching staff a new way of working with clients (eg: Milne 1985). The author is aware from experience of instances where Snoezelen has been used inappropriately, for example, as a 'time out' room for disruptive clients, or a place where clients can be left for long periods without supervision. Such practice may be frightening and distressing for the individuals concerned and provides a stark contrast to the philosophy behind the approach. The development of Snoezelen constitutes an attempt to improve life quality for a much neglected client group and it would be sadly ironic if misuse of the approach resulted in the opposite effect. The design, implementation and thorough evaluation of training packages for care staff may play a vital role in ensuring the Snoezelen environment fulfils the purpose for which it was intended.

## Acknowledgements

The author would like to thank Dr Derek Milne, Department of Clinical Psychology, University of Newcastle upon Tyne and Steve Noone, Clinical Psychologist at Prudhoe Hospital, Northumberland for supervising the study reported in this chapter. Most of all, my grateful thanks to Fiona Nelson and Sue Gerrie, Occupational Therapists at Prudhoe Hospital for their help and support and all the care staff and residents who participated in the study.

### REFERENCES

1    Anderson S R. The Management of Staff Behaviour in Residential Treatment Facilities: A Review of Training Techniques. In Hogg, J and Mittler P (eds), Staff Training in Mental Handicap, London, Croom-Helm (1987).

2    Baker B L. 'Parents as Teachers: a Programme of Applied Research'. In Milne, D (ed) Training Behavioural Therapists. Croom-Helm, London (1986).

3    Cullen C, Burton M S, Watts S and Thomas M. A Preliminary Report of the Nature of Interactions in a Mental Handicap Institution. Behaviour Research and Therapy, 21: 579-583 (1984).

4    Cullen C. Nurse Training and Institutional Constrains. In Hogg J and Mittler P (eds) Staff Training in Mental Handicap. London, Croom-Helm (1987).

5    Cullen C. A review of Staff Training: The Emperor's Old Clothes. Irish Journal of Psychology 9.2: 309-323 (1988).

6    Cunningham C. Recreation for People with Profound Learning Disabilities and Multiple Handicaps. Unpublished Research Protocol, North Derbyshire Health Authority (1989).

7    Daily E F, Allen G J, Chinski J M and Veit S W. Attendant Behaviour and Attitudes Toward Institutionalised Retarded Children. American Journal of Mental Deficiency, 78: 586-591 (1974).

8    Dalgliesh M and Matthews R. Some Effects of Staffing Levels and Group Size on the Quality of Day Care for Severely Mentally Handicapped Adults. British Journal of Mental Subnormality, 27: 30-35 (1981).

9    Farrell P T (ed). E.D.Y.: Its Impact on Staff Training in Mental Handicap. Manchester University Press, Manchester (1985).

10   Farrell P T. 'Teachers as Therapists: an Account of the E.D.Y. Project'. In Milne D (ed) Training Behaviour Therapists, London, Croom-Helm (1986).

11    Gardner J M and Giampa F L. The Attendant Behaviour Checklist: Measuring On the Ward Behaviour of Institutional Attendants. American Journal of Mental Deficiency, 5: 617-22 (1971).

12    Gelfant D M, Gelfand S and Dobson W R. Unprogrammed Reinforcement of Patient Behaviour in a Mental Hospital. Behaviour Research and Therapy, 5:201-207 (1967).

13    Green B F, Willis B S, Levy R and Baily J S. Measuring Client Gains from Staff Implemented Programmes. Journal of Applied Behaviour Analysis, 1:395-412 (1978).

14    Haggar L E and Hutchinson R B. Snoezelen: An Approach to the Provision of a Leisure Resource for People with Profound and Multiple Handicaps. Mental Handicap, 19:51-55 (1991).

15    Harmatz M G. Observational Study of Ward Staff Behaviour. Exceptional Children, 39:554-558 (1973).

16    Hogg J and Mittler P. Staff Training in Mental Handicap. London, Croom-Helm (1987).

17    Hulsegge J and Verheul A. Snoezelen: Another World. Rompa UK. (1987).

18    Hutchinson R B (ed). The Whittington Snoezelen Project. North Derbyshire Health Authority (1991).

19    Jones A and Robson R. Within Course Effects of a Training Package for Teachers of the Mentally Handicapped. Special Education, Forwards Trents: Research Supplement, 10:17-20 (1983).

20    Jones A A, Blunden R, Coles E, Evans G and Porterfield J. Evaluating the Impact of Training, Supervisor Feedback, Self Monitoring and Collaborative Goal Setting on Staff and Client Behaviour. In: Hogg J and Mittler P (eds): Staff Training in Mental Handicap, London Croom-Helm (1987).

21    Landesman-Dwyer S and Knowles M . Ecological Analysis of Staff Training in Residential Settings. In: Hogg J and Mittler P (eds) Staff Training in Mental Handicap. London Croom-Helm (1987).

22    Lobitz G K and Johnson S M. Normal versus Deviant Children: A Multi-Method Comparison. Journal of Abnormal Child Psychology. 3:353-374 (1974).

23    Meinhold P M and Mulick J A . Counter-Habilitative Contengencies in Institutions for People with Mental Retardation: Ecological and Regulatory Influences. Mental Retardation 28, 2:67-75 (1990).

24    Milne D. An observation Evaluation of the Effects of Nurse Training in Behaviour

Therapy on Unstructured Ward Activities and Interactions. British Journal of Clinical Psychology, 24:149-58 (1985).

25    Milne D. An Ecological Validation of Nurses Training in Behaviour Therapy. Behavioural Psychotherapy, 13:14-28 (1985).

26    Milne D. The More Things Change, the More They Stay the Same: Factors affecting the Implementation of the Nursing Process. Journal of Advanced Nursing, 10:39-45 (1985).

27    Milne D. A Review of the In Service Training of Nurses in Behaviour Therapy. Behavioural Psychotherapy 13:120-131 (1985).

28    Milne D. Training Behaviour Therapists: Methods, Evaluation and Implementation with Parents, Nurses and Teachers. London Croom-Helm (1986).

29    Milne D. Planning and Evaluating Innovations in Nursing Practice by Measuring the Ward Atmosphere. Journal of Advanced Nursing, 11:203-210 (1986).

30    Milne D. Training Others in Behaviour Therapy: A Dead Duck? In: Eisenberg N and Glasgow D (eds) Current Issues in Clinical Psychology. Gowerver, Aldershot (1988).

31    Moss R H. Evaluating Treatment Environments: a Social-Ecological Approach. Wiley, London (1974).

32    Moos R H. The Human Context: Environmental Determinants of Behaviour. Wiley, London (1976).

33    O'Dell S L, O'Quinn J A, O'Briant, A L, Bradlyn A S and Giebenhain J E. Predicting the Acquisition of Parenting Skills via Four Training Methods. Behaviour Therapy, 13:194-208 (1982)

34    Parket R M and Thomas K R. Fads, Flaws, Fallacies and Foolishness in Evaluation of Rehabilitation Programme. Journal of Rehabilitation, 46:32-34 (1980).

35    Parson M B, Schepis M M, Reid D H, McCArn J E and Green C W. Expanding the Impact of Behavioural Staff Management: A Large Scale Long Term Application in Schools Serving Severely Handicapped Students. Journal of Applied Behavioural Analysis, 20:139-50 (1987).

36    Paton X and Stirling E. Frequency and Type of Dydacdic Nurse-Patient Verbal Interactions in the Mentally Subnormal. International Journal of Nursing Studies, 11:135-145 (1974).

37    Paul G L and Lentz R J. Psychological Treatment of Chronic Mental Patients. Harvard University Press, Cambridge (Mass) (1977).

38      Quilitch H R. A Comparison of Three Staff Management Procedures. Journal of Applied Behavioural Analysis, 8:59-66 (1975).


39      Rawlings S A. Lifestyle of Severely Retarded, Non-Communicating Adults in Hospitals and Small Residential Homes. British Journal of Social Work, 15:218-293 (1985).


40      Rojahn J, Mulick J A, McCoy D and Schroeder R R. Setting Events, Adaptive Clothing and Modification of Headbanging and Self Restraint in Two Profoundly Retarded Adults. Behaviour Analysis and Modification, 2:185-196 (1980).


41      Sanson-Fisher R and Jenkins H J. Interaction Patterson Between Inmates and Staff in a Maximum Security Institution. Behaviour Therapy, 9:703-716 (1978).


42      Whaler R G and Fox J J. Solitary Toy Play and Time Out: a Family Treatment Package for Children with Aggressive and Oppositional Behaviour. Journal of Applied Behaviour Analysis, 13:23-29 (1980).


43      Willems E Q. Behavioural Technology and Behavioural Ecology. Journal of Applied Behaviour Analysis, 7:151-175 (1974).


44      Woods P A and Cullen C. Determinants of Staff Behaviour in Long Term Care. Behavioural Psychotheraphy, 11:4-17 (1983).


45      Wright E C, Abbas K A and Meredith C. A Study in Interactions Between Nursing Staff and Profoundly Mentally Retarded Children. British Journal of Mental Subnormality, 20:14-17 (1974).

*Appendix 1*

<u>Sample of Questionnaire Used in Training Evaluation, to Measure Staff Knowledge About and Attitude Towards the Snoezelen Concept Before and After Training.</u>

(Examples of correct/acceptable responses are given in brackets, as is post training format).

**SNOEZELEN QUESTIONNAIRE**

Before you begin (now you have completed) the Snoezelen training, I would like you to try and answer the following questions about Snoezelen (again). This is not a test or examination - your answers will help me make sure I include (have included) the right sort of things in the training package. Don't worry if you do not know the answers - just write 'don't know' in the space provided.

1       Snoezelen consists of 4 different things. Can you name any or all of them? (Leisure for client/resident, sensory stimulation, relaxation, individual attention).

2       Where does Snoezelen originate from? (Holland).

3       What sorts of special equipment and effects would you expect to find in a Snoezelen Room? (Bubble tube, fibre optics, relaxing music, ball pools, coloured lights, etc - any 2 or more listed constitutes 'correct' responses).

4       It is thought that Snoezelen is a good idea for profoundly and multiply disabled people. Please say whether you agree with this, disagree, or are unsure. (Broad 'attitude' measure, eg 'agree' response constituting positive attitude, 'disagree' constituting negative attitude).

5       Please say why you agree/disagree. (Supporting, qualitative measures).

6       Please think of a resident with you who is very disabled. How might you use a particular piece of equipment imaginatively, to help this resident enjoy their time in a Snoezelen room? You may choose any piece of Snoezelen equipment of 'extra' you know (have learned about). ('Creative' use of equipment question, with 'correct' response incorporating stimulation of more than one sense, eg: bubble tube, could be used to provide visual, auditory and vibrotactile stimulation).

7       Supposing you could not afford proper Snoezelen equipment for your home, but you had a small amount of money to spend and a small areas to use. What sorts of things could you buy, or use to improvise Snoezelen with? Please list as many things as you can think of. (D.I.Y. Snoezelen question, with more than two items constituting 'correct' response. Examples include Aromatherapy oils, 'disco' spotlights which change colour, pieces of fur fabric for tactile stimulation, etc).

8       Please list the kinds of things you think you would need to know, in order to ensure your residents get the most out of Snoezelen. (Please list any improvements you think could be made to my Snoezelen training package). (Needs assessment/feedback item).

### Categories of the Attendant Behaviour Checklist and Adaptations Used in the Study (* = Adaptation)

| Category | Definition | Examples |
|---|---|---|
| 1 Supervision | Providing protective care of client | Watching, telling client to do something. *Observing safety within Snoezelen, eg: preventing client from chewing or biting electrical equipment. |
| 2 Personal Care | Caring for clients bodily needs | Dressing, wiping nose |
| 3 Socialization | Engaging in warm interpersonal relations | Recreation, talking in friendly manner *Using equipment to provide sensory stimulation |
| 4 Punishment | Actual or threatened abuse, physical or verbal | Hitting, raising hand. *Excluding from Snoezelen |
| 5 Training | Teaching new skills, rewarding old skills | Teaching self care or social skills. *Teaching client how to use Snoezelen equipment. |
| 6 Rejection | Lack of acceptance, physical or verbal | Ignoring reasonable requests, avoiding physical contact. |

### Sample of Training Satisfaction Questionnaire

### SNOEZELEN TRAINING SATISFACTION QUESTIONNAIRE

Please help me improve my Snoezelen training package by answering some questions about the Snoezelen training you have received. I am interested in your honest opinions, whether they are positive or negative. Please answer all of the questions. I also welcome your comments and suggestions. Thank you very much - I appreciate your help.

Please circle your answer

1) How would you rate the quality of the training you received?

| 4 | 3 | 2 | 1 |
|---|---|---|---|
| Excellent | Good | Fair | Poor |

2) Did you get the kind of training you wanted?

| 4 | 3 | 2 | 1 |
|---|---|---|---|
| No definitely not | No not really | Yes generally | Yes definitely |

3 To what extent did my package meet your needs?

| 4 | 3 | 2 | 1 |
|---|---|---|---|
| Almost all of my needs have been met | Most of my needshave been met | Only a few of my needs have been met | None of my needs have been met |

4 If another home needed Snoezelen training, would you recommend my package to the staff ?

| 4 | 3 | 2 | 1 |
|---|---|---|---|
| No definitely not | No I don't think so | Yes I think so | Yes definitely |

5 How satisfied are you with the amount of training you received?

| 4 | 3 | 2 | 1 |
|---|---|---|---|
| Quite dissatisfied | Indifferent or mild | Mostly satisfied | Very satisfied |

6 Do you think the training you have received has helped you use Snoezelen more effectively with residents?

| 4 | 3 | 2 | 1 |
|---|---|---|---|
| Yes it helped a great deal | Yes it helped somewhat | No it really didn't help | No it just confused me |

7   In an overall, general sense, how satisfied are you with the training your received?

| 4 | 3 | 2 | 1 |
|---|---|---|---|
| Very satisfied | Mostly satisfied | Indifferent or mildy dissatisified | Quite dissatisfied |

8   If new members in your home needed Snoezelen training, would you ask for my package again?

| 4 | 3 | 2 | 1 |
|---|---|---|---|
| No definitely not | No I don't think so | Yes I think so | Yes definitely |

Please write any other comments below:

## Appendix 4

**Sample of short structured interview, conducted at 6 week follow up with staff**

**STRUCTURED INTERVIEW**

1      What do you find satisfying about your job?

2      What do you find frustrating about your job?

3      When the Snoezelen room is built in the home, do you think it will change any of these things?

4      Please think of a resident you have 'Snoezeled' with. Can you tell me how this resident usually responds when you interact with them eg: at mealtimes, bathtimes, in the day room?

5      Please tell me how the resident responded to Snoezelen?

6      Do you think your residents will benefit from Snoezelen in the home? Please say why/why not.

# PEOPLE WITH A DISABILITY - THERAPISTS AND SENSORY ACTIVITY

Anita Moore
Gill Harris
Judy Stephens

Everything that we know of the world around us comes from the impingement of stimuli on the sense organs. The most important are of course, vision and hearing, but receptors in the skin, nose and mouth are also significant.

In addition to these, the kinaesthetic sense provides feedback during learning performance of motor skills. Kinaesthetic and static senses play an important role in facilitating general body co-ordination (very important for visually impaired people).

It follows then that the person with profound sensory disabilities is limited in his/her ability to make sense of the world and consequently, frustration, depression and confusion become the norm. Many users of the sensory environment have both profound sensory disabilities and intellectual impairment and are also at a proverbial stage of development where they are further restricted in their abilities to learn new information through verbal language.

Use of vocabulary related to the senses therefore becomes redundant and physically experiencing sensation becomes paramount.

## Physiotherapy

The role of the psysiotherapist in learning disabilities is to assist an individual to improve the quality of their life by achieving their optimum physical potential. Besides treating acute physical injuries, the physiotherapist will assess and advise on the management of chronic conditions. This can be done through assessment leading to a plan of action or treatment which is evaluated after a specific time. Often acute injuries can go untreated by generic services due to behavioural problems which prevent either appropriate access to treatment or refusal to be examined. In these cases, Snoezelen can be used to create the right environment to allow examination and subsequent treatment, eg: using the White room or the jacuzzi area to relax the individual and give them the confidence to be examined. From my experience, disabled people who use our specialist physiotherapy service and do not have an acute injury, fall into four broad categories. These categories often have very similar aims of treatment. However, the means of achieving these aims will differ greatly depending on a variety of factors. These include the individuals ability to communicate/express their wishes and to understand the reason/need for treatment.

Even though I will talk about people in these four categories, it must be stressed that each client should have an individual physiotherapy assessment. This should be used in conjunction with other assessments to give a balanced overall picture of the person and their needs.

The categories are :

People with a:    A)    Profound physical and mental disability

                 B)    Profound learning disability

                 C)    Physical disability with a learning disability

                 D)    Learning disability without a specific physical disability.


**A    *Profound Physical and Mental Disability***

Besides severed intellectual impairment this group suffer from damage to the motor area of the brain leading to alterations in muscle tone, eg: spacticity. They have little or no volitional movement. Movements that they do have are usually non functional. This group often suffer from epilepsy and have other sensory defects, eg: visual problems and communication difficulties.

**Main Aims of Physiotherapy Intervention**

1    To prevent or slow down the development of contractures and deformities.

2    To develop volitional movements.

3    To improve general fitness and sense of well being.

**Means**

1    Good positioning - lying, sitting, standing.

2    Good handling.

3      Encouraging activities which promote movement and facilitate basic body responses ie: equilibrium and balance reactions.

4      Interaction/Communication through movement.


B      *Profound Learning Disability*

This group suffer from gross intellectual disability but their physical disability is minimal. They often have active movements but these are stereotyped and non functional.

**Main Aims of Physiotherapy Intervention**

1      To prevent deformity

2      To shape volitional movements leading to function

3      To improve general fitness and sense of well being.

**Means**

1      Encouraging activities which promote movements and facilitate basic body resposes, eg: rebound therapy.

2      Promoting activities which are positive, pleasant and fun which can lead to functional movement, eg: bathing.

3      Interacting and communicating through movement, eg: mat work.


C      *Physical Disability with a Learning Disability*

This group usually have less severe physical difficulty than Group A and a reasonable level of understanding and communication.

**Main Aim of Physiotherapy Intervention**

These are the same as for Group A

**Means**

By identifying specific goals to achieve the aims. The client can be involved in making choices about treatment and their active involvement in this, eg: exercise routines.

**D** *Learning Disability but without a Specific Physical Disability*

This group consists of people who have behavioural problems. People with minimal physical disabilities such as poor co-ordination, unsteady gait, poor dexterity, minor alterations in muscle tone or both.

**Main Aims of Physiotherapy Intervention**

1    Identify specific physical deficits.

2    Improve general fitness and strength.

3    Improve physical skills and self confidence.

4    Improve posture and body image.

5    Improve communication skills through movement.

**Means**

1    By identifying specific goals and devising methods to achieve these.

2    Giving advice and guidance on involvement with sports/leisure pursuits.

3    Supplying specialist equipment to enable participation in activities.

**Traditional Methods of Techniques used by Physiotherapists to Achieve these Aims**

1    Relax inhibiting postures, eg: good head position to reduce extensor spasticity.

2       Vibration.

3       Massage - Clinical
                Sensory.

4       Sensory stimulation, eg: tapping, clapping.

5       Rebound therapy

6       Horse riding

7       Hydrotheraphy/Swimming

8       Exercises - mats
                balls
                rolls.

9       Parachute.

10      Passive movements.

11      Veronica Sherbourne techniques

12      Circuit training

13      Weights

14      General fitness programme, eg:  walking, running, jogging

15      Outdoor pursuits

16      Supply of Equipment, eg:    walking frames
                                    standing frames
                                    wheelchairs
                                    moulds

17      Orthotics - eg: boots and calliper braces.

## Difficulties/Limitations of these Traditional Treatments and Techniques

1    Identifying the correct stimulus which will lead to the wanted response.

2    Providing this stimulus and making it acceptable to the client.

3    Funding equipment especially if required in a number of areas,
     eg: work, place, home.

4    Maintaining and storing equipment.

5    Having equipment in the right place at the right time - many therapists work at a
     number of sites or storage is away from the treatment area.

6    Finding space to work without interruptions and for the desired length of time -
     by the nature of the clients disabilities, this is often very variable and therapists
     may have to vacate rooms at the critical moment.

7    Using public facilities, eg: Leisure Centre, Pool.

**Requires**

Enough staff at the right time with the right skills.

Transport and driver.

Appropriate changing facilities, eg: benches to lie one.

Right sex staff for the client in the changing rooms.

Warm enough water.

Access to the pool, eg: may need a hoist.

Space to work in the pool without being drowned by exuberant children!

Access to the pool, eg: time when you also have staff available.

These are just a few of the obstacles that need to be faced before an activity can take
place.  The other difficulty is the successful integration of clients into social

environments so that it is positive for the clients and the public. Very aberrrant behaviour can be extremely detrimental to this integration.

## How Snoezelen Helps Benefit the Therapist

From the list at the beginning of the chapter, it can be seen how access to a Snoezelen environment can alleviate many of the limitations of working in a non purpose built environment.

### Assessment

As a physiotherapist, I find Snoezelen especially beneficial for assessment. It provides limitless opportunities for observation and subtle intervention. Clients who find it difficult to understand the purpose of activities/requested /desired during assessment, often do the activities naturally during Snoezelen activities. The fact that activities are not stressful means that movements are not tense and artificial, giving a clearer picture of ability levels.

### Teaching

This non stressful environment provides opportunities for teaching carers and families new handling and positioning techniques and new ways to relate to clients. In a Snoezelen environment, it doesn't matter if the client refuses an activity by screaming or shouting, therefore carers and families are happier to attempt new things.

### Moving On

Snoezelen can be used as a gateway, by shaping clients behaviour they can be introduced to few activities in public places, eg: using the jacuzzi in Snoezelen may lead to confidence in using the jacuzzi in the leisure centre.

### Instant Access

Access to facilities at the times that is right for the client is invaluable. We often need to act quickly on an individuals mood to be able to capitalise on this and develop new skills.

## A Physiotherapists View of Things to Consider in a Snoezelen Environment

1  The relationship of one room to another, eg: from a jacuzzi area to move directly to a restful area without breaking the moods is valuable.

2  The relationship of rooms and corridors, entrance and exit to each other:

    a)    Should there be more than one way in or out of a room?

    b)    Could entrance or exist to a room be achieved without breaking the mood of the room? eg: tunnels.

    c)    Should we have different surfaces or two ways of getting around? eg; firm one for wheelchairs or trolleys, soft one for crawling.

3  Moveable floor surfaces to allow firm surfaces to replace soft surfaces to facilitate transfers.

4  Varied height rests and supports which could help to assist transfers, allow good oppositioning and promote movement, eg: soft bench to allow ease of transfer from one level to another, possibly with a slope at one side to aid getting to and from floor level.

5  The use of slopes built into the ball pool to assist transfers in and out.

6  Various height padded leaning places so that people can lean or stand or kneel with minimal assistance

7  A wider variety of movable supports to allow people to experience movements, eg: hammock, swing/slides.

8  Other methods of moving people around without constant lifting, eg: trolleys - padded built-up side - various heights, scooters, soft rugs to drag people along on.

Having experience Snoezelen, I feel that many of the movement experiences that we could facilitate are lost or diminished because immobile clients are lifted from area to area. If some of the previous ideas were introduced, I feel that movement potential could be maximised in conjunction with enhanced sensory experiences.

## Advantages of Working in a Snoezelen Environment

1    The environment has a positive image and is valued by others.

2    No social norms of behaviour are compulsory.

3    The environment is suitable for all levels of disability and all age groups.

4    Snoezelen staff are sympathetic to the philosophy of sensory activities.

5    There is no stress as there are no set expectations.

6    Achievement and success are possible even to the most profoundly disabled person.

7    The facility is interesting, exciting, relaxing, friendly and safe.

8    The positive aspects of Snoezelen can be used as a reward, before, during or after other therapeutic intervention.

9    Everything is together, ready for use, regularly maintained and designed for robust use.

10    The positive aspects of the Snoezelen Centre can be harnessed by the therapist to shape behaviour. The level of anticipation, excitement etc felt by the client is all valuable to the therapist.

11    There are no interruptions when working.

12    The therapist can observe without intervention.

13    The space and type of activities means that clients and carers aren't as aware of observation as they may be in a small department, therefore more natural activities occur.

14    A therapist can intervene without intruding on an activity.

15    The environment and atmosphere can easily be altered before and during sessions to promote specific activities.

16    The environments lend themselves to both group and individual work.

17    The Snoezelen is a safe, flexible, stimulating environment where anything goes - the therapist can use this to get the full value from their training to develop skills and technique which will enhance the quality of life of handicapped individuals. Giving renewed hope and stimulus to families and carers who felt that traditional services had passed their people by.

## Conclusion

There are no really new ideas or techniques in Snoezelen. It is the concept which makes it so valuable. As a therapist, I feel that it can assist us in making more effective use of our skills and act as a catalyst to others learning and developing these skills.

Looking at a profoundly disabled person in a new way after seeing them in a Snoezelen environment will lead to an improved quality of life not only for the person but for staff whose work with that person will be far more rewarding.

## OCCUPATIONAL THERAPY

In order to learn, develop and be motivated, we all need stimulation. We receive this stimulation in our daily lives through our primary senses, eg: sight, smell, taste, touch, hearing and movement. It is via these primary senses that the brain gathers information from the outside world and is stimulated to respond. However, a person who has mental, sensory or physical handicaps is not able to absorb this information correctly.

Such a person may suffer from a wide range of handicaps.

These include:

*    Restricted physical movement - varying from reduced use of one limb to limited purposeful use in all limbs.

*    Cognitive deficits - including poor memory, concentration and attention.

*    Perceptual difficulties - the person being unable to interpret and understand information received about shapes and objects.

* Communication difficulties - the person may not be able to use verbal communication of any type or to understand people when they talk to him. In addition, the person may not be able to take in non-verbal communication, eg: gestures. Other disabilities such as poor eye contact and poor concentration may contribute to problems in communication.

* Impairment of one or more of the primary senses - the individual may for example have visual or hearing problems.

With all, or some of these handicaps, the person is unable to explore, collect and process the stimulations usually experienced in daily life. The ability to learn and develop from the environment is therefore reduced. In addition, in some environment, the actual sensory stimulations may be restricted to those received during direct basic care - dressing, toileting, bathing and eating. Other sensory activities such as those encountered when out of the living area may be rare, hence limiting the individual's experiences, learning and stimulation.

## Planning

When commencing sensory work with someone with profound multiple handicaps, it is important to consider several points, including:

* The individual and worker need to have a rapport with each other. The worker needs to be able to identify the person's feelings towards the stimuli and the individual needs to feel relaxed and have confidence in the worker.

* Timing of sessions - eg: avoiding periods when the person may be tired such as after a swimming session.

* Choice of rooms - a quiet undisturbed room with which the person is familiar. If the sensory environment area is "new" to the person, it may be appropriate to allow him several sessions purely to become accustomed to the setting.

* Positioning of the person - this is especially important if the person has physical disabilities as certain positioning may increase the person's physical abilities as well as comfort, and therefore motivation.

*   Length of session - this will depend on each person and their level of concentration which may range from seconds upwards. If someone has very limited levels of concentration, it is recommended to work with them for short but frequent spells of time rather than one long session.

*   Be aware of the person's needs, feelings and events. If for example the person had a restless night, they might require more of a relaxing session and it might not be a good day to be expecting the person to take an active part.

*   Work at the person's own pace, and keep expectations realistic - do not expect miracles!

*   Give lots of praise and appropriate rewards.

*   The session should be enjoyable - if someone is having fun they will be motivated to participate and learn from the experience.

## Primary Senses

With sensory activity, we are encouraged to stimulate and investigate the individuals primary senses and to consider each of the primary senses carefully. Previously, we may not have considered each of the senses so specifically.

Whilst it is important to consider all of the primary senses separately, as described below, it must be stressed that they do not operate separately but interact. For example, the sense of smell makes an important contribution to what we perceive as taste. That is why food does not taste so good when our nose is blocked.

## Sight

This includes those who are blind, partially sighted, as well as those who may lack the cognitive ability and motivation to user their sight. By using sensory activities, it may be found that someone who was originally thought to be totally blind does in fact respond to a certain colour or shade.

For those who are not motivated to use their sight, they need to be stimulated to do so.

Other stimuli will need to be "blocked out" and a dark room used where a large bright object, such as a bubble tube, is turned on. The person should be encouraged to look at it as well as feel it to promote stimulation through touch as well. Eventually, smaller objects can be used and very gradually, normal lighting conditions introduced by making the room progressively light (dimmer light switch, opening curtains/doors a little more as progress is made.

Once the person is able to look or "fix" on an object when it moves. These eye contact skills need to be continued in everyday skills, for example when eating, the person needs to be encouraged to look at the food on his plate and "track" the spoon from the plate to his mouth.

Finally different lighting can have quite dramatic effects on the behaviour of some people. For example, varied light patterns projected on a wall in a softly light comfortable room may relax the most boisterous of people.

**Taste**

Discovering someone's favourite tastes enhances our understanding and knowledge of that person. By giving the person the opportunity to taste different types of food, their awareness and experiences increase. This may also lead to their ability to make informed choices about what they would like to eat. "Tasting sessions" need to be done at appropriate time and places, ie: meal times, snack times. The individual needs to be encouraged to use his other senses as well - to look at the food, to smell the food. Not only should all different tastes be tried including sweet sour, etc but also different textures, consistences and temperatures. For example, different flavoured:

> Beverages - teas, coffees, juices, pop, milk shakes
> Soups, dips
> Ice cream, lollies
> Yoghurts
> Jams, preservatives etc.

"Taster sessions" could be organised or even special buffet meals provided with a wide variety of different tastes. Meals out would also encourage greater experience not only for different tastes but a wealth of other sensory stimulation.

**Smell**

This is a powerful sense and one which we need to work on more. Even modern day museums are now incorporating this to enhance their scene setting displays such as the Yorvik Viking Centre, York and Robin Hood Experience, Nottingham.

Once someone's preference are discovered, they can be used to promote the person's functional ability. Consistent use of a particular perfume by one individual may promote recognition of that person. Specific smells in different rooms can promote location of these rooms, eg: pine in the toilet, pot pourri in the sitting room.

When trying out different fragrances with someone, it is recommended to try a few at a time with intervals of at least a minute between each. This is to ensure the effectiveness of the stimulation.

## Hearing

The person may have a physical hearing impairment or they may not have the cognitive ability or motivation to listen. In order to investigate these difficulties, all type of sounds should be tried - varied pitches, tones, rhythms, music and silence. When initially working on these sounds, the use of a dark room with all the other stimuli "blocked off" may be necessary. Eventually, contrasting sounds will need to be introduced to encourage discrimination. Sound tracking and location of the sound will also need to be worked on.

## Touch

We learn a lot about our environment from touch. There are numerous different types of textures including rough, smooth, soft, hard, wet, dry, warm, cold. The individual should be encouraged to touch things in everyday life, eg: different textured clothing, temperature of water when washing hands, warm/cold air from hairdryer/fan heater, leaves, bark of tree. Also everyday objects can be gathered together and used to encourage touch, for example: cotton, wool, feather duster, string, door mat, brushes, ice pack. Touch from other people is also very important such as during massage and jacuzzi sessions.

## Movement

By encouraging the person to move in an energetic way or in a relaxed passive manner, their "vestibular" and "proprioceptive" senses are stimulated. The vestibular sense is the balance mechanism site inside the inner ear and constantly gives feedback about balance and head position. The proprioceptive sense gives us information about the position of our limbs. There are small sensory fibres located at all joints and muscles and when these fibres are lengthened or shortened, information is sent to the brain so that we can interpret the position of our arm, leg, etc. So a person who is non-ambulant and multiply disabled, may have minimal opportunity to gain this stimulation but by doing activities with carers such as swimming, sliding, rolling, rebound therapy, this stimulation is received.

## Control of the Environment

With sensory environments, opportunity is also given to people to have control over their environment with the use of pressure pads, for example, to operate equipment. This may be the only time they are physically able to control what happens to them. It also introduces an element of choice and learning the skill of cause and effect, ie when the pressure pad is touched, the wind machine goes on.

## CONCLUSION

All people need stimulation. In its absence, individuals may resort to self injury, anger or repetitive behaviour as a substitute. Therefore, the exposure to a wide range of sensory stimulation should be the cornerstone of treatment designed to reduce, avoid or channel these traits. Indeed, for those who have profound sensory, physical and mental disabilities, the only way of stimulating them and getting the brain to respond is through the primary senses.

# THE SPEECH AND LANGUAGE THERAPISTS CONTRIBUTION

The Speech and Languages Therapist's ultimate aim in intervention is to improve global communication skills in order to minimise the problems caused by restricted communication. He/she must therefore make optimum use of differing modes of communication to improve comprehension skills and function language. Improvement in these and other social skills will be dependant upon training being given in the following four main areas:

1  Foundation Skills - such as eye contact, appropriate posture, attention control. In order to encourage and expand these skills, it is obviously important to establish rapport and develop common interests with a client. If your client has few needs, preferences or interests, then he/she will have little or nothing to communicate about. Within the Snoezelen facility mutual experiences of social contact, music, lights and other experiences which are likely to be pleasant or interesting can be gained and become part of the communication programme. Part of this strategy will involve encouraging and allowing **CHOICE**, where the client can begin to see that he/she can influence others' behaviour - a very powerful social asset.

2  Affective skills - such as sharing feelings, expressing emotions and recognising others problems. By identifying and adapting a client's expression of emotion during exploration of the sensory environment, eg: laughing, crying, kicking, grabbing, etc the Therapies may be able to turn a non-communicative act into one of intent.

3  Interactive/interpersonal skills - such as initiating and maintaining communication. At a preverbal level, this may include purposeful touching or pointing to an object, glancing at an object and then at the Therapist to indicate 'give me' or simply looking at an item. Positive interaction can thus be developed.

4  Cognitive skills - such as reasoning, predicting outcomes and understanding cause and effect. There are many and varied opportunities within the sensory environment where these skills can be encouraged, eg:          light and sound floor
                                                          ball race
                                                          ..... tracking systems

It is important for the client to realise that even a small amount of input on his/her behalf can result in change and he/she has been instrumental in that change. What a moral booster!

Many of these preverbal and verbal skills can be encouraged and improved by selective use of equipment in the sensory environment.

Therapeutic intervention becomes more positive and rewarding for the client when it occurs in a relaxing and pleasurable setting. It is possible, with a degree of imagination, to utilise a wide range of therapy techniques to effect positive change in a person's approach to communication. If this equates with fun, then it is more likely to be learnt and the client better motivated to go further.

## Assessment

We need to discover what functional use a person is making of his primary senses in order to understand his skills and needs. Hearing for instance may be intact but if selective listening is not taking place, then communication via the auditory channel becomes severely restricted. Comprehension of speech will be impossible if a person cannot discriminate between one sound and another. As with hearing and listening, if a person can see but not interpret the object, then the visual channel cannot be used to any effect.

Other sensory agnosias may be present, the effects of which may be minimised by developing a programme of intervention centred on a specific sense.

The sensory environment lends itself very well to informal assessment of communication skills:

a)     it is non-threatening

b)     it is rich in sensory experience

c)     it offers plenty of opportunity for extended
       observation of a client's behaviour.


## What do we need to assess in order to develop programme for intervention

1              Hearing and Listening

2    Vision and Looking

3    Expression of Emotion

4    Non-verbal Communication -

   a)    Gestures
   b)    Pointing
   c)    Pushing
   d)    Manipulation of others emotions
   e)    Vocalisation

5    Positive/Negative Interactions

6    Motor and Vocal Imitation

7    Communicative Intent

8    Modes of Communication

9    Functional Language

Therapeutic intervention can then take place in a secure, safe and above all, enjoyable environment where repetition of 'tasks' does not become boring. Uncluttered by extraneous distractions, the Therapist (and client) can concentrate on a specific activity and achieve more positive results.


## Uses of the Sensory Environment in Specific Disabilities

### Visual Impairment

1    Tactile/kinaesthetic feedback

2    Exploration

3    Fuller use of the auditory channel

4    Less stress

5    Teaching of specific vocabulary eg: hard/soft, rough/smooth

6    Interactive communication

7    Positive, self-contained pleasures

8    Concept development eg: prepositions/plurals/adjectives

9    Space perception
     - an intersensory affair - other senses provide spatial
        information:- olfaction; temperature;
        kinaesthetic/static senses

10   Use of olfactory sense to locate environment/people.

**Auditory Impairment**

1    A stress-free environment in which to explore changing visual stimuli.

2    Interactive communication.
     - encouragement of non verbal modes,        eg:    signing
                                                        what's this?
                                                        where is?

3    Concept development

4    Use of secondary senses, eg: tactile

5    Stimulation of any residual hearing.

## Eating and Swallowing Disorders

As a large proportion of taste is smell, heightening awareness of this sense has often resulted in improved eating skills. Our sense of smell is 10,000 times more sensitive that taste and the human nose can identify up to 400,000 odours. Smelling and odour can re-create powerful visual imagery, not only of a place in the past but of emotions felt at that time. It can evoke memories and encourage vocalisation. verbalisation.

For the person with profound learning disabilities or visual impairment, smells can be used to enable identification of location, people and, to become more aware of their environment.

More able users who have no obvious sensory impairment can develop:

1    Relaxation techniques - useful in anxiety stress:
     challenging behaviour.

2    A wide range of vocabulary within a stress-free
     environment.

3    Logical reasoning skills

4    Self-reinforced learning.

A purpose built sensory environment offers a secure, stimulating and exciting facility where learning new skills becomes fun.

Although for some people verbal communication may not be an option, the use of multi-modal multi-sensorial stimulation can help effective functional communication to develop.

Individuals may develop methods of effecting change expressing choice and feelings, of initiating and terminating a communication act or simply a way of saying, 'I'm here,' 'I want to communicate with you'.


**SUMMARY**

There has been some debate as to how the two concept of leisure and therapeutic interventions can possible be compatible.

Many leisure pursuits enable us to grow in confidence and gain new skills within an environment which is non-threatening, motivating and enjoyable. It may be that the 'non-compulsory' aspect of leisure activities and the fact that we have personally opted to pursue something which we perceive as fun, is part of the attraction.

Whatever the reason for our valuing our leisure time, we would recognise that it brings a break from routine and a time either for reflection or a change to 'do something completely different'.

All these are possible in the sensory environment. Therapeutic intervention within this environment can be seen as an extension of leisure - it achieves the same aims and much more, making the clients quality of life richer.

Opportunities can be given through sensitive programmes to enjoy all of lifes experiences with more insight and in a more positive way, be it as 'work' or play.

### References

Norris David, Profound Mental Handicap, Pub. Costello Educational (1982)

Finnie Nancie R, Handling the young cerebral palsied child at home, Pub. Heninemann Medical Books 2nd ed (1974)

Bobath B, Bobath K, Movement Development in the different type of cerebral palsy, Pub. Heinemann Physiotheraphy (1985)

Levitt S, Treatment of cerebral palsy and motor delay, Pub. Blackwell Scientific Publications 2nd ed (1982)

Sherbourne Veronica, Building Relationships through movement, with special reference to children with communication problems, Creative Therapy (1975)

Sanderson H, Gitsham N, A Holstic Approach (1991)

Playtrac, A brief instruction to augmented mothering, Harperbury Hospital (1989)

Rustin & Kuhr, Social Skills and the speech impaired

Kiernan & Reid, Pre Verbal Communication Schedule (1987)

Anderson Helen, Making Sense of Scents: Therapy Weekly 17 October 1992

# SNOEZELEN AND SELF INJURY

## Dana Henning

The focus of this chapter is the application of Snoezelen techniques and philosophies to the treatment of people with profound intellectual disabilities who display self-injurious behaviour. This chapter is not meant to be an introduction to self-injury or to Snoezelen as it is assumed that the reader has at least a working knowledge of both areas. The purpose here is to apply the principles of Snoezelen to a specific need. This chapter will provide a cursory discussion of self-injury and how it effects the life conditions experienced by a person with self-injury may unintentionally be contributing to the problem and move quickly into how Snoezelen can provide support to these individuals.

### Potential Causes of Self-injury

There are many theoretical causes of self-injurious behaviour (Baumeister 1976). Through the year professionals have considered everything from medical problems, mental health issues, operant conditioning, seizure activity, to attempts on the part of the individual to communicate his needs and/or control his environment. Each of these theoretical causes leads one to a logical assumption as to how the self-injury should be treated. Most likely, each of the treatments have proven to be successful in ridding some individuals of self-injury. Unfortunately, despite these efforts, there are still many people who self-injure on a regular basis (Repp & Singh 1990).

In addition to the more medical and theoretical outlooks, the practitioner also needs to consider how some of the more practical day to day experiences of people with profound intellectual disabilities may be unwittingly contributing to self-injury. Several inter-related areas must be considered here.

One issue that underlies most others is the lack of personal relationships. Many people with profound intellectual disabilities were separated from their families early in life and have repeatedly dealt with the loss of people as staff and room mates have come in and out of the person's life. Just as the person would become comfortable with someone, they would be gone, often without a word. Forming relationships is not typically easy for these folks who have a minimum of communication skills and experience at initiating relationships. Few people both are available in this environment and capable of forming a relationship. Frequent trips to a medical centre or to physical therapy sessions taught the lesson that too often physical contact with another human being results in physical discomfort or pain. After a while, many people with these experiences withdraw from others and turn inward for stimulation and comfort.

Group living can often result in a lack of control. When many people live together there must be some procedures in order to manage. As a result, people often have little control over the choice of their room mates, the time meals are served, what is served, how and by whom.

People are often moved from place to place with little understandable explanation or opportunity to object. Privacy may be only an occasional treat. Many of these living situations are one extreme or other, other-stimulating or deadly quiet. These conditions are not designed to be negative and in fact, may appear quite luxurious to one upon first inspection of a lovely, newly decorated facility, but one needs to pause and imagine the situation from the eyes of the people who live there. What would it really be like to live here?

Many facilities would lovingly accommodate a person's individual desires but all to often the person has no means of expressing them. Although augmentative and facilitated communication techniques have assisted many people, there are still vast numbers of people who have not generally understood methods of communication. This results in a lack of control over the day to day as well as the more global issues in one's life. The stress and frustration that would result from these circumstances is obvious.

Facilities required by regulation of funding authority, as is often the case in the United States, to provide Active Treatment, often unintentionally add another stressor into the lives of people with profound intellectual disabilities. Active Treatment requires that the person be assessed by an interdisciplinary team in order to create an integrated list of the person's strengths and needs. Although not the intent of the regulations, 'needs' often translates into those things which the person cannot do. Goals are then developed to address each of the areas cited in the person's need first. Staff must provide ongoing treatment in each goal area. Treatment is provided in both day and residential placements. In theory this sound wonderful. However, perhaps it is not wonderful to the person receiving the treatment who, because his waking hours are spent working on goals, in essence gets to spend his entire day and night doing things he is not good at doing (if he was good at doing it, he wouldn't have a goal on it). The unintended outcome here is that he spends his day doing things he does not enjoy for few people enjoy doings those things they do poorly.

Opportunities for leisure are very limited for many people experiencing these difficulties. Many people lack the skills necessary to participate in the activities others enjoy for leisure times; participation in these activities too often means further instruction and pressure rather than relaxation and enjoyment. Even people who find golf relaxing, remember back to the frustration, not relaxation involved in the initial learning of the skill. Here may have been the need to relax after the leisure activity!

In some facilities, leisure opportunities are used as reinforcement, ie the person is allowed to participate in leisure activities if he has completed other tasks or perhaps as a positive consequence for the absence of his self-injury over a given period of time. Misbehaviour results in a loss of leisure time. Although theoretically well-supported in the behavioural literature for the person involved, it means that he will only be granted leisure on "good days" - and it is human nature to need an opportunity to relax most desperately on our worst days!

These issues have not been mentioned to lament the problems within programme services for most of these problems arise despite the best of intention and despite the quality of the services being received. These are not problems resulting from abuse or neglect but rather as the unintentional side effect of group living and the careful balance of continual treatment for long term improvement with a personal quality of life on a day to day basis. These issues have been raised to remind the reader what it might be like to live in a facility from the perspective of the people being served. Think of the stress, the lack of control. Imagine how frustrating it would become. Now, isn't there the possibility that some of these stress factors could be contributing to some of the self-injury being done?

**What does Snoezelen have to offer people who engage in self-injury?**

Snoezelen is a controlled environment. With the assistance of a training staff member the person can create the type of environment best suited to his personal tastes. He can spend quality time with a staff member he trusts, someone who both understands him and is free to respond to his non verbal communication. Self-injury is dealt with indirectly, by looking at the larger picture of the person' environment and life circumstances rather than focusing in on a direct treatment for a specific self-injury. He can control the environment. He can do or he can not do. He can relax. There is no pressure. He is not being instructed. He can just be.

The ability to control his environment: In a Snoezelen room, the environment is changeable and can be modified to suit the needs of each guest. A person can "see" sounds by making a sound into a microphone attached to an interactive sound and light wall. Sound, motion, or pressure mat switches all enable the person to create a breeze, change a slide visual, control the sound system, or sniff a favourite fragrance. Through a sound, grimace or body tension, the person can let staff know that he dislikes something and that something can be changed! A smile, a grasp, or a bit of muscle relaxation can let the care giver know that something is being enjoyed. That which is enjoyed does not need to be earned by compliance, task completion or absence of a target behaviour. Enjoyment is freely given and shared.

One of the benefits of Snoezelen is the control of the environment. Now think of this benefit of Snoezelen in terms of a person who is currently using his self-injury to control his environment. Think of a person who is placed in a time outroom when he self-injures; could this person be thinking, "In order to get into that nice quiet little room, I need to hurt myself", for in fact, privacy is the reward here for self-injury. Think of a person who is unable to call a friend to his side but is able to get every staff person in the room to his side by banging his head hard enough on his wheelchair tray. Think of the person who cups his hands and smacks his head in order to block out the noise of his day activity room. These folk may be effectively using self-injury to control a seemingly uncontrollable environment. Snoezelen shows them another way to control the environment that doesn't have to hurt.

The opportunity to build a relationship: Time in the Snoezelen room for a person who self-injures is an opportunity to be alone with a care giver. The importance of the emotions passed between care giver and care receiver are all too often overlooked or underrated. In some agencies, staff are continually assigned to different people. Sometimes this is done intentionally so that people do not form attachments. People who don't have relationships with others are more likely to experience problems relating to depression. Since the relationship between depression and self-injury has also been recognised (Dosen & Menaloscino 1990), the relationship and warmth shared with onespecial staff member could help the person to find some relief. In the Snoezelen room, the care giver and receiver share the experience together. A relationship builds to help the person develop or regain a sense of trust and comfort with others.

The opportunity to touch and be touched. People need human contact. Unfortunately for many people with profound intellectual disability, human touch has often been accompanied by the pain of physical positioning, medical treatments, etc. Some people have found that if they begin to hurt themselves when a staff begins to touch them, the staff member will go away. Whereas this does establish some control in the person's life, and a sense of being able to stop the "bad" touch, it also acts to eliminate the good touch. Restraints almost appear to replace the need for human contact for some people who experience the most difficulty. Temple Grandin in her book entitled **Emergence: Labelled Autism (1986)** describes a cattle harness that provided her with "hugs" that she could control and obtain without the need of touching another person. Snoezelen offers a time and place to touch and be touched in a painless way. Various physical positions on bean bag chairs, on water beds, on boulders allow for physical contact. The addition of a Jacuzzi room, Snoezelen provides the added sensation of experiencing warm, rushing,

*WHITTINGTON HALL*

*SENSOKIT*
*SPASTICS SOCIETY - CHESTERFIELD*

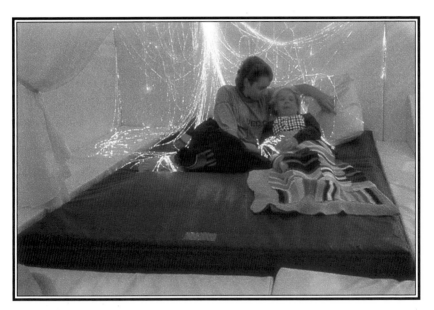

*WATER MATTRESS*
*WHITTINGTON HALL*

*BALLPOOL*
*WHITTINGTON HALL*

*CASCADING FOUNTAIN*
*SPASTICS SOCIETY - CHESTERFIELD*

*VIBRATING CUSHION*
*KINGS PARK - BOURNEMOUTH*

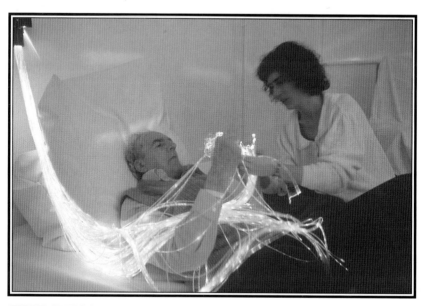

*FIBRE OPTIC SPRAY*
*KINGS PARK - BOURNEMOUTH*

whirlpool water to be shared with a friend. Aromatherapy and Massage (Sanderson et al 1991) done with the needed medical approvals can enhance the experience while maximising the relaxation opportunities for a person. Many people who have spent years in restraints will stop injuring themselves if restraints are removed slowly by the process of a massage by a qualified and trusted person. It seems to be human nature to "mellow out" when being massaged in a safe, quiet environment and it is often difficult to get up the energy to continue hurting yourself when you feel so mellow!

A chance to increase or decrease the stimulation in the environment: People are frequently bypothesized to self-injure because of inadequate or an overabundance of sensory stimulation. Often this was an accurate observation but other than offering the person some textures to feel or a vibrator to touch, the practitioner was at a loss as to what could be done based on this insight. Snoezelen offers the opportunity to provide the type of stimulation the person enjoys while eliminating the stimulation he find annoying. Because all elements in a Snoezelen room can be controlled, the environment can change one element at a time.

This opportunity for total environmental control also allows for a careful assessment of what seems to upset the person and result in self-injury and which elements help the person to relax. This information in itself can be invaluable. With this knowledge, the care giver or treatment team can return to the person's daytime and residential environment and begin to modify both to comply with the person's needs. In many cases, it is not an agency's unwillingness to increase or decrease the stimulation in an environment that is the problem but rather the lack of knowing which things to keep and which things to change within the environment. The diagnostic information gained from the Snoezelen room would help with these changes. Such changes within the daily environment are likely to assist the person in gaining control over his self-injury throughout his day.

A time to unwind: Most people feel rejuvenated after a leisurely weekend. Snoezelen provides the same opportunity to people with self-injury. As it seems logical that self-injury would increase when one feels stressful, it follows that decreasing stress would help to decrease self-injury. Snoezelen offers a slow pace, safe environment where the person can unwind. Very often the person will calm down enough to allow partial or total removal of restraints and remain calm without restraint while in the Snoezelen room.

Will the relaxed feeling generalise to the person's environments? It depends! There are many differences within individuals and these differences change over time. Just as with the general population, some people unwind over the weekend and can maintain the calm throughout the work week; other people may unwind and enjoy the relaxation of their weekend but begin to tense as soon as they walk into their office on Monday morning. Likewise, some people mellow out in the Snoezelen room and are able to maintain that calm until their next visit whereas others may return to self-injury as they leave the Snoezelen room. It is also not unusual for a person to unwind and stop self-injury in the Snoezelen room and begin to self-injure on a more intense level upon return to his regular environment. If this occurs, you can generally assume he is giving you a very strong message concerning what he likes in his environment and that those elements are lacking in his day to day environment. When this happens, one must do whatever possible to modify the person's day to day environment so that it contains those elements in the Snoezelen room that the person needs and does not contain those elements that contribute to the person's self-injury. It is not possible to modify the entire environment, an alternative is to modify the person's sleeping environment or to use the Snoezelen room just prior to bedtime. At bedtime, almost all environments slow down so there is a natural setting for relaxation. A good nights sleep is something many people do not take for granted and providing a refreshing sleep may in itself improve the person's quality of life and ability to relax throughout the day.

Clinicians can become frustrated when the Snoezelen room is able to stop the self injury while the person is in the Snoezelen room but does not generalise to other settings. It is frustrating, there is no doubt, especially when you would like to modify the other environment and are powerless to do so. There is a tendency to want to terminate access to the Snoezelen room when the relaxed behaviour does not generalise to the other environments and to conclude that Snoezelen does not "work" for that person. This is an unfortunate conclusion. Given that no techniques, medication, etc has worked to stop the self-injury but there is a least momentary relief in the Snoezelen, most people, if able to voice their preference, would select the partial relief over none. As information and technology in this area increase, there may be more to offer a person with these problems but until such time, let's not lose sight of the goal to improve quality of life where possible.

**Some suggestions for using Snoezelen with people who self-injure**

It is assumed that the people who are considering using these techniques are familiar with both Snoezelen and with working with people who self-injure. Therefore, the suggestions here do not address either of those issued in depth but rather focus specifically on application of Snoezelen to people who self-injure.

1      People who self-injure often find it is difficult to trust new people
        or to feel comfortable in new places. Therefore, if a person is

comfortable with a particular staff person, that is likely to be the best staff member to introduce the person to Snoezelen. However, don't assume that merely because a person is familiar with a staff member that they have a comfortable relationship. The ideal staff person is one who is able to decrease the person's self-injury by his mere presence or even voice tone, someone who in his arms the person's body naturally relaxes. This staff member can be trained in Snoezelen or "talked through" the activities until he feels comfortable working independently with the person.

Some people who self-injure don't seem to respond to any particular person. A person in this situation may do best by starting a new relationship with a staff member that is initially exclusive to the Snoezelen room. The staff member who works in the Snoezelen room would work to create a sense of security, a knowing that nothing in the Snoezelen room will be painful or unpleasant. For the person with no positive relationships, it is better to disengage and to show the separateness of Snoezelen rather than relating to and building on the less than positive relationships in other environments. This may take a little longer initially but is likely to develop into a more trusted relationship. As time goes on and a good relationship has developed with the Snoezelen staff member, other staff can very slowly be introduced in an attempt to generalise that sense of trust.

2      Begin the first visit to Snoezelen room in a dimly lit, quiet room. The person should be the only participant in the Snoezelen room. As the staff member you want to be available to the person but must avoid violating the person's personal space. Don't come close to the person unless he indicates it is acceptable to join him. If you come near and the person tenses, slowly back away, reassuring the person that you are there if he needs you. All conversation should be quiet, calm and comforting. Reassure the person; tell him he will be safe and he will be cared for. As the person seems to be relaxing as indicated by a less tense body position, pleasant sounds and/or a relaxed facial expression, try adding some soft music. If the person seems to enjoy the music, continue. If not, try different types of music, try different headsets, speakers etc. Assess which music seems best for the person and then provide that music.

After the staff person is well versed in the person's musical preferences, begin to add another element, perhaps visual stimulation. Again, experimentation is the key word while responding to the person's indications of preference - try a wide selection, but quickly stop those things the person seems to dislike. As you add in the second element you may find that some people only like one type of stimulation at a time, others only like certain elements combined or only if they are synchronised. Be sensitive to the issue that some people prefer to be in a particular position in order to enjoy something. It is helpful to initially write yourself short notes in order to have this information for the person's next visit and to be able to share this information with the staff caring for the person in other environments.

3    If the person is willing, gradually begin to share his space. If the person tenses, slowly back away. Each person is different. For some people, it is best to sit or lie along side the person and quietly talk without touching. For other people, it helps to quietly rub lotion into their arms, hands, etc. Still others will tolerate your presence if it is quiet, still and does not involve touching them. If the person reaches out to you or touches your arm be sure to respond in a like manner. Perhaps the person is willing to allow touch if he initiates it himself but not if the staff member does - that is fine, too. Some people will let you into their space during the first visit, others will only open up after numerous visits with the same staff person.

4    If the person has a helmet or wears restraints when he enters the room, let him settle in before beginning to remove the helmet or restraints; they may be providing a sense of security to the person. As you feel the person beginning to relax, try gently rubbing his hand with lotion. When using lotion, try to avoid any "standard issue" lotions used elsewhere in the facility as they my bring back unpleasant memories. Try to find a lotion or oil (Jackson 1991) that is special to the Snoezelen room.

Can you get the fist unclenched? Can you get him to extend his arm for you to continue? As the person begins to smile, roll towards you or give you any other signals that you are pleasing him, try to slowly loosen and gradually remove a portion of the restraint. Of course any agency or treatment team approvals would be necessary before beginning this process. If the person tenses or begins to self-injure, stop removing the restraint, wait and then begin again, more slowly. Sometimes all you are able to do initially is to loosen the restraints but keep them in place. Remember that this is a slow process and slow progress is better than no progress. Everyone has good and bad times so do not assume that you will always be able to remove the same amount of restraints or for as long of a time period. The longer the person knows you and you know him, the easier this will become. After a time, the person may be able to spend his entire time in the Snoezelen room without restraints. Trust is very important here.

5      "Leading" is a concept in which the person gets involved in an activity, be it watching a bubble tube or turning a fan off and on, and the staff joins in. This in itself will be a new experience for some people who are used to having tasks presented to them by staff and they respond rather than the other way round. The goal here is to have the person take the initiative. The staff person needs to be mindful not to invade the person's personal space by being too enthusiastic to "share" or to accidentally take charge over the activity. It is the person's activity, the staff person is the invited guest and as such you cannot force that invitation. If the person is unwilling to share, back away and respect the person's privacy. If the person is willing to share, follow his lead; at a comfortable point, try to "lead" the person into another activity. You share with the person. When he begins to share, you follow. It is a reciprocal process. Let the person set the pace. See what he is interested in and then follow that lead. Avoid the traditional care giver role in which the staff initiate all activities to the person. Remember that the purpose of leading is two fold: to decrease self-injury by building a trusting, sharing relationship and by returning control to the person.

6      Since many people who self-injure (particularly in the United States) live in agencies which must comply with Active Treatment which requires continual instructions in areas of need and documentation of progress, keep in mind that you can make Snoezelen into legitimate goals and provide documentation if you are required to do so.

Remember the key is that the goal must match the stated need. If the need is to decrease self-injury and the goal is to increase choice, the "need" and the goal don't match. However, if the need is to express choices as a key to decreasing self-injury and the goal is to increase expression of choice (by indicating preferences within the Snoezelen room), you have a match that licenser will appreciate. Be creative.

Document the number of choices made, the number of objects presented as options (a choice among 3 options is a more advanced skill than choice among 2 options), the type of communication shared with staff, the number of actions initiated or terminated by the individual. If you are measuring the self-injury, do not forget to include measures of duration, intensity, generalisation, etc and as well as measuring a newly acquired skills, eg: reaching out for your hand or an object, gently pushing your hand away, indicating pleasure of displeasure without need to resort to self-injury.

7    Snoezelen seems to work best for people whose self-injury is a function of stress, depression, lack of stimulation, over stimulation, lack of personal warmth from another human being, lack of control, fear and mistrust of others. It may be helpful, (or even necessary to accommodate regulations) to complete a functional analysis of the self-injury in order to better understand what is behind the self-injury. The insight will help you to plan activities that will best address the persons' identified needs. There are many types of functional assessments commercially available (laVigna & Donnellan 1986; Meyer & Evans 1989) or it may provide helpful to create one specific to your agency's needs.

8    Snoezelen does not usually work well for self-injury directly related to seizure activity. If working with someone with seizure activity, even if controlled by medication it is very important to get approval from a physician to be certain that the lights of Snoezelen will not trigger seizure activity. It is also vital for the staff members working in a Snoezelen room to know what to do in case of a seizure.

In conclusion, the use of the Snoezelen room has been a welcome addition in servicing people with profound intellectual disabilities who are troubled by self-injury. It is not a panacea. It does not stop all self-injury. It sometimes is able to prevent self-injury for the person only while he is in the Snoezelen room and does not generalise to other environments. There is still much to learn in the area of self-injury. Over time, there will be new treatments and medications that will help more people. However, in the meantime, Snoezelen has demonstrated its ability to provide relief to some people who are causing themselves the most damage. It has offered a "mini vacation" to people who experience great stress in day to day life. Snoezelen offers staff a new way to relate to and understand the people they serve. Despite the theories, the treatments and the medications, there are still people out there in pain. Snoezelen offers them another hope.

**References**

1    Baumeister A A & Rollings J P. Self-injurious behaviour. In NR Ellis (ed) International Review of Mental Retardation, Volume 8 (pp1-34) New York: Academic Press (1976).

2    Dosen A & Menolascino F J (eds). Depression in mentally retarded children and adults, Leiden, The Netherlands: Logan Publications (1990).

3    Grandin T & Scariano M M. Emergence: Labelled Autistic, Novato, CA: Arean Press (1986).

4    Jackson J. Aromatheraphy, Ringwood, Victoria, Australia: Penguin Books Australia Ltd (1986).

5    LaVigna G W, *Donnellan A M. Alternatives to punishments: Solving behaviour problems with non-aversive strategies. New York: Irvington (1986).

6    Meyer L H & Evans I M. Nonaversive intervention for behaviour problems: A manual for home and community. Baltimore MD: Brookes (1989).

7    Repp A C & Sngh N N. Perspectives on the use of nonaversive and aversive interventions for persons with developmental disabilities. Sycamore III: Sycamore Publishing Co (1990).

8    Sanderson H, Harrison J & Price S. Aromatherapy and massage for people with learning difficulties, Lutterworth, Leicestershire, UK: John Abbott Printers Ltd (1991).

# SENSORY ENVIRONMENTS - A MANAGEMENT PERSPECTIVE

## J Kewin

*A Managers perspective including an account of the Whittington Hall Project and its success in winning the 1992 National Health Services Journal Management Award (Community Health Care Category)*

## BACKGROUND

As changes are taking place within the caring services, expectations have risen. Within services for people who have Learning Disabilities this has happened more quickly. Perhaps the speed of change or expectation of change is due to these services starting from a lower base line of provision. People who have had either the most "challenging behaviour" or the most profound disabilities have often received the least resource. In part, this has been due to traditional funding methods, but there has also been a lack of appropriate "services, techniques and things to buy". Whilst traditional nursing, caring and paramedical services have been steadily improving, they have not caught the imagination sufficiently enough to bring about a revolution in care practices. This appears to have happened due to the "normalisation and quality" initiatives of recent years. The Better Services type documents appear to have been recognised and there is now a feeling of some urgency for change.

If ever there was a optimum time to request better provision and changes in attitude for people who have sensory and learning disabilities, it is **NOW**. In addition to this mood for change, there are also physical changes that can be provided that can be seen to demonstrate increased quality of provision.

A simple but useful way of looking at this is to use one of the recognised motivational factors in human behaviour. These principles are currently featured in management training and therefore should be a common source of understanding between carers and managers. Maslow referred to a "hierarchy of human need" where he describes physiological, safety and security, social status, and self-actualisation as the stages that we need to progress through to meet levels of need. In most care situations for people who have profound disabilities, we may be able to truthfully say that we only meet either the first or second level on the hierarchy. In part, this is due to resourcing but also to our inability to communicate effectively with the individual. As a result, effective social contact and personal development is often out of reach.

## ATTITUDES AND CULTURE

Once basic care has been secured, it is now considered to be a fundamental human right to allow people leisure time or opportunities for self expression. Pleasure, stimulation and involvement are derived from interacting with the world around us. This in turn depends on the use of the senses. The more opportunity there is to practice these skills the more chance we have of being accepted as interesting human beings in our own right. Unfortunately, the care culture has often directed us to "get on with the basic care". It takes considerable courage and changes in management expectations to encourage and support carers who wish to move to a more "humanistic way of caring". Managers need to give the clear message that they expect change, and support carers in this approach. It is asking too much of staff of low status to change the culture or caring organisations from the bottom up. It is far easier for this to happen from the top down.

## SENSORY ENVIRONMENTS

Once the principle of gaining access to the senses has been accepted as invaluable, the opportunities are endless. Bathrooms can be made more stimulating, television can give way to simple lights on the wall, therapy sessions can include a wide variety of sensory stimulation. In addition to these changes, the development of specific sensory rooms popularised by the "Snoezelen" concept seems to have caught the imagination.

In working in these facilities, there are some fundamental points to note that may ensure a better and more effective use of the facilities and the energies of those involved.

## ATTITUDE

Carers, therapists and helpers may require training to standardise the positive approach needed to free up inhibitions. Enjoying the world through the wonders of the senses is what we should be aiming for. This cannot happen in an atmosphere of tension or where restrictions are placed on the individual.

It is crucial that managers and senior staff adopt this philosophy in order that it can successfully permeate through the care organisation.

## SUPPORT

Staff engaged in moving towards methods of providing sensory experiences will need to exchange the safe role of the production of items such as pictures of finished products for the production of a good time or good feelings. This requires considerable support in valuing this activity. This support comes through an understanding of the benefits to both the carer and the recipient.

## OPERATIONAL ISSUES

Adapting existing facilities with lights and sounds should make few demands for maintenance or over expensive equipment. When we consider the major change in "atmosphere" that can be generated, this is a small price to pay. In the case of major developments in rooms for sensory activities there needs to be considerable thought to the administrative or generalised issues. These will include:

a)    Managerial commitment

b)    Initial funding

c)    Location and access

d)    Maintenance and replacement of equipment

e)    Common philosophy of use
        Risk taking - policy
        Emotional/sexual expression - policy

f)    Access - opening times - who can use it

g)    Structure - who's in charge

h)    Support from senior professionals for staff

i)    Clinical or service audit

j)    Cleaning

K)    Administrative consideration, eg: fire - safety

l)    Public access - liability, etc

## EVOLVING AN OPERATIONAL POLICY

The most effective way to evolve a workable operational policy is to involve all the key individuals and professionals in sharing their views and expectations. The Commitment gained in this way can ensure ownership of the philosophy and this will be of greater value to the person in charge.

Staff employed in services are our major resource and their level of motivation will help to determine the degree of quality of the services provided. Whilst financial factors and working environmental factors are important to all staff, it is recognised that those who work with people who have profound disabilities also gain great satisfaction from knowing that their contribution to the individual's quality of life is valued. Well planned additions to services in the form of sensory experiences can give a valuable books to routine experiences and so motivate people to more creative exploration.

## A FURTHER INSIGHT INTO MANAGERIAL MOTIVES

The very nature of organisational structures and managerial cultures appears to create communication barriers between the very people who are changed with the responsibility for performing a given task. How often have we heard it said, "Its a good idea but how can we get it past our Manager?" This question has constantly been raised on every major Sensory and Snoezelen training course and workshop run at the Whittington Hall facility in Derbyshire.

Course participants from a wide variety of backgrounds and agencies appear to have a similar problem or fear in taking their creative ideas back to their workplace and turning them into actual benefits for service users.

This chapter explores a real situation and examined the Managerial motives behind the implementation of a very successful Sensory project. It may give some clues to the key issues facing Managers and in doing so it may help readers to frame their case of need or sharpen their arguments for developing projects.

The example given is of a Service for People with Learning Disabilities run by a Health Authority. The Management model used is the Nadler and Tushman Diagnostic Model of Change. This model provides a way of looking at organisations of varying sizes and exploring the component parts in order to take account of all the important issues during a major change. The model or variations of it are taught to Managers within the major care agencies and it acts as a good check list in ensuring that important aspects of the service are given appropriate consideration.

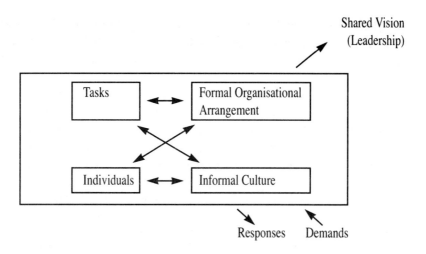

Shared Vision
(Leadership)

Tasks ←→ Formal Organisational Arrangement

Individuals ←→ Informal Culture

Responses   Demands

The Nadler and Tushman Diagnostic Model

The organisation responds to demands made from others and it gives responses. Where the organisation may wish to go is referred to as the Shared vision. The changes that are necessary to take all the very important component parts across to the new service or the shared vision do not usually happen by chance but are enabled through a Leader.

In our case, the organisation was a major Health Service for People who have Learning Disabilities. Whilst the Service had a reputation for providing good care, many staff felt devalued due to the advances being made towards Care in the Community in other parts of the service. This had an important and worthwhile benefit to those who had moved from the institution but the economic climate did not allow for the successes to be shared by all. People who required greater financial resources had to wait until funding packages had been developed in order for them to move to the new vision.

Staff were left to struggle on with basic facilities feeling that they had been abandoned by Managers who were focusing their attention on the new and aesthetically pleasing aspects of the community developments.

National and Regional policies and initiatives kept up the pressure for the Management of the service to move towards what was seen to be the new model of service provision. Other significant initiatives that were present at the time were the emergence of Quality and Personalising services for Staff and Patients. By appreciating the current 'favours of the month' it was possible to frame a case of need for the development of a Centre for Sensory activities. In all aspects of new service bids, this is a necessary component for success. By reading and interpreting the opportunities of the day, it is possible to key into resourcing. Without this approach, we may be dependent upon an influential backer finding the resources necessary.

## The Task

This was to provide the best possible care and opportunities for people with given resources. In moving towards more appropriate Community models of care, it became very obvious to Managers and staff that meaningful activity, leisure and therapy were provided in minimal quantity and quality for those people who were profoundly and multiply disabled. The quality of life for the individual was poor and this was highlighted when we compared lifestyles at institution and community level.

If we were to improve the quality of life for each individual, we had to explore new ways of providing improved quality in areas of personal contacts with other people in the environment itself.

## Individual Providing Care

Demoralised and devalued were expressions used by staff to describe how they felt when they had been left to carry on inside an ageing institution within a framework that now suggested that the models of service provision of the past were no longer valued.

Between sixty and seventy per cent of all staff had no formal qualifications yet people and their personal motivation are the single biggest asset that the organisation possesses in providing the service. Commonly heard comments such as, "No one cares about our part of the service" and "There never seems to be anything done for people who have the most profound disabilities" were reflections of genuine feelings born from years of experience. The anxieties of staff towards the changes and due to low financial investment, was being felt by Managers and the Authorities through crisis meetings with staff organisations and through articles in the local press.

As with any other large organisation, there were people who had retained their creative spark and there were those who would put up partial resistance to change.

## The Formal Organisational Arrangements

Management structures and the processes of decision making tended to lend themselves to maintain the status quo whilst still being open to change due to the problems that were being experienced within the service.

## The Informal Culture

By its nature, the culture of 'the way we do things around here' had evolved over many years and it was resistant to change. Whilst the institutional culture was very evident in aspects of daily life, staff wanted to provide the very best care and life experience for people.

## The Shared Vision

The vision of the new service in the community with everyone having an improved quality of life was not shared by many of the staff who remained within the service. They were suspicious of Managerial changes and a lack of positive responses to suggestions and initiatives to improve the quality of life of the people who remained.

## Leadership

This was provided through a General Manager and ex-clinician who worked through a number of other service managers.

## Managing the Change

A deliberate decision was made to make the maximum use of the experience and energy of the staff. Initiatives would be encouraged and areas of real concern to people regarding the quality of life of those in their care would be given priority. This had the effect of winning over the majority of Senior and influential staff. One of the major concerns of the staff was the lack of appropriate meaningful activity for the most disabled individuals within the service.

Carers were motivated by providing and being associated with good service. It was evident that focusing attention on improving the quality of life of clients would also improve the moral of staff and managers.

A visible and usable vehicle of change was need and the Snoezelen project was chosen although the dramatic effects of its influence could not be predicted at the time of initial investment.

As the project fathered momentous and people started to share the vision, it was possible to detect changes in attitude. Comments such as, "It's about time they did something for our people" and "How soon will the place be ready?" had replaced the earlier concerns. Press coverage of the initiatives was sought and all articles after the commencement of the project showed the service in a good light.

Staff who could be a potential benefit or hindrance to the new project were involved in training and policy writing. This again shared the vision and made maximum use of their skills and experience whilst ensuring that the resources were used to best effect.

Communication with staff, Managers and the Public was felt to be of prime importance and this helped to change peoples perceptions of the service. Unexpected changes in the culture of the service were evidence from an early age. The initiatives were carried into the Ward areas with the development of decorations and rooms. Nursing baths were replaced with jacuzzies and, lights and plants were added to Bathrooms and Toilets.

In the Day Care and Leisure areas there were remarkable improvements in staff morale. Absence from sickness improved dramatically and staffing remained stable for the following three years.

A major research project involving many direct carers was commissioned by the Health Authority and the resultant interest and involvement shown by staff created the impetus for the next stage of the development. The experience gained was shared with other services which highlighted the positive aspects of our own service. Interest from further afield and from other agencies encouraged the Professional staff to design and run workshops and training for other people. This has the effect of providing good publicity for the service and also maintaining the interest and skills of our own staff who are frequently challenged by the questions posed by visitors.

Making the Most of the Benefits

A further deliberate effort to utilise publicity and Managerial initiatives was made in 1992 when the project and its positive achievements were entered for the National Health Service Journal Management award. The entry entitled "Snoezelen - a gently revolution in Care Practice' won the first prize in the Community Health Care Service category.

The Future

On completion of the Institutional changes, the Health Authority encouraged the inclusion of a new and extensive Sensory Centre in the new replacement service. This includes over one acre of sensory gardens.

Through the opportunities available within the new management arrangements within

NHS Trusts, the service is currently exploring the possibility of creating a total living environment, holiday and assessment service. The creativity that this has harnessed provides positive encouragement for those involved and allows others to be carried along in the wake of the ideas and their benefits.

Managers of major agencies are taught to consider changes and developments in a systematic and thorough way. When resources are scarce, it is necessary to put strong arguments forward in order to secure approval and commitment. Practical experience has shown that well thought out cases of need that can demonstrate the benefits of all aspects of the service have a better chance at gaining support.

Like you, Managers are concerned about the quality of the services that they are responsible for. They need to demonstrate that resources are being used effectively. The biggest resource in any caring agency is its staff and their positive motivation is essential if they are to be enabled to utilise their skills and experience to maximum effect. The Snoezelen concept has facilitated a great deal of change in the service considered here, perhaps more importantly, it has enabled staff to harness their motivation by providing creative, quality experience for those people with the most profound and severe disabilities.

*ELDERLY, FURNITURE*
*KINGS PARK - BOURNEMOUTH*

*ELDERLY*
*KINGS PARK - BOURNEMOUTH*

*FIBRE OPTIC SPRAY, BUBBLE UNIT*
*SPASTICS SOCIETY - CHESTERFIELD*

*FIBRE OPTIC SPRAY*
*LIMINGTON HOUSE*

*BUBBLE TUBE*
*LIMINGTON HOUSE*

*FIBRE OPTIC SPRAY*
*LIMINGTON HOUSE*
PHOTO - S. CLIMPSON

SNOEZELEN IN EDUCATION

Marilyn Gallaher
Mervyn Balson

*An account of the setting up and development of Snoezelen in a school for children with severe learning difficulties*

SNOEZELEN IN EDUCATION

This is not an authoritative study of Snoezelen in education but rather a description of the use of Snoezelen and it's philosophy in helping to meet some of the educational, social and emotional needs of the children within a school for pupils with severe learning difficulties (SLD). It is not our intent to present a study of the literature concerning sensory stimulation and the needs of the SLD school publication. Although much has been written about the senses, little has been published on the development and application of the sensory curriculum for our group of children. Rather than simply giving a list of references supporting our work at Limington House, we would much prefer to suggest the reader consults Flow Longhorn's excellent book 'A Sensory Curriculum for Very Special People' (Longhorn F (1988). A Sensory Curriculum for Very Special People, London Souvenir Press). It is a catalogue of suggestions supported by references and contact which we feel we could not better. The work marks one of the few attempts to draw together ideas on the sensory curriculum and as such is invaluable as a resource in its own right.

It is important that we briefly describe our School. Although it has a small boarding element, a unit placed with a local mainstream comprehensive school, and a further education facility, the bulk of the day provision is we feel, much like any other local authority SLD school. Limington House is a school for children aged 2-19 years who have severe learning difficulties. Of the 120 places at the school, 20 are for termly boarders. As with many SLD schools, we have a growing population of children with profound and multiple learning difficulties (PMLD). At present, almost 30% of our children have profound multiple learning difficulties. The school is maintained by Hampshire County Council. Local Education Authority funding is supplemented by private and charitable sources of income. Since April 1992, Limington House has been given a delegated budget as part of a County local management of special schools (LMSS) pilot scheme.

The arrangement of teaching groups within the school is largely aged based, with the overall organisation reflecting the main age phase of Primary, Secondary and Further

Education. Although we have no discrete PMLDD Department, we do have PMLD class bases located in the different age phase areas of the school building. Dependant on their levels of ability and need, PMLD pupils may link into one of our 'main' teaching groups for some part of their day/week. For some of our PMLD pupils, their level of need and vulnerability means that they spend all of their time within a dedicated PMLD group. Pupils who have physical difficulties but whose intellectual abilities put them within the 'main' teaching group bands are not considered to have profound multiple learning difficulties and are thus placed within the 'main' groups. We also have a group dedicated solely to extreme challenging behaviour where a clearly differentiated programme of study is undertaken by each child with the main emphasis geared to behaviour management.

The school operates within the framework of the National Curriculum as appropriate to individual child needs. A core school Curriculum augments the National Curriculum and covers all aspects of intellectual, physical and social development. A part of the school character is that staff and parents are always seeking ways to enhance the curriculum and other opportunities on offer to the children.

Whilst the school had always placed great emphasis on the delivery of sensory activities, especially for the PMLD children, we found ourselves searching in 1989 for a way of providing a sensory environment for assisting the staff in delivering sensory activities aimed at both stimulating and relaxing various groups and individuals. Along with support from the Parent Teacher Association of the school, staff visited and researched a number of sensory systems. Up until this point, we had 'played around' with sound and dark rooms but with our having no coherent philosophy to support the work we were doing, other than our own desire to broaden the experiences we were giving the children. We already had a sensory curriculum but were unsure of how to integrate this into a sensory environment. Looking back, we can appreciate just how amateurish and ill thought out some of our sensory 'experiments' were!

Following a period research into various options for constructing a dedicated sensory environment, we decided that what was needed was for us to develop a Snoezelen room and to base the use of it and our approach to other aspects of sensory work broadly on the Snoezelen philosophy. At this stage, we were very clear in wanting a stand alone Snoezelen facility but had certainly not fully appreciated the implication of the underpinning Snoezelen philosophy - a point that will be discussed later.

Our fortunes took a marvellous leap forward in 1991 when we were awarded grants from The Allied Dunbar Foundation and our local radio station Radio 210, which with some additional fund raising enabled us to extend the school building to provide an architect designed sensory facility. This consists of a Snoezelen room and large soft play room. The Snoezelen room has a fully padded floor with the walls being padded to half their height. The room is light tight and has an array of auditory, visual and knaesthetic pieces of equipment. The soft play room is fully padded and contains a vast amount of soft and padded structures including a ball pool, all of which very usefully augments the dedicated Snoezelen room.

The new building was purpose designed by the County Architect's Department. The structure is of a similar scola nature as the rest of the school. All the glass in the building is armoured with windows in the soft play room being designed to be above the height of the wall padding. The heating system can also blow cold air, is instantly controllably and positioned high up on the room walls. The ceiling is beamed so as to support a variety of hanging structure capable of taking the loading of an adult. All power points and switches are at shoulder height. The room lighting is contained within reinforced tubes so as to avoid damage from objects being thrown or swung about. The fire alarm system works by auditory and visual warning. The architect liaised closely with Rompa (the chosen suppliers) to ensure that equipment and padding would fit snugly into the rooms. The sensory building was opened just before Christmas 1991 by the broadcaster Dr Hilary Jones.

Of course Snoezelen is not a new concept. It is however, relatively new in being used as an educational tool. At present, a number of special schools in the United Kingdom and other countries are beginning to realise the potential of using Snoezelen in helping to meet the educational needs of children with severe and complex learning difficulties. Snoezelen can be a difficult concept for educationalists to grasp. It may appear on the surface as a very fancy and somewhat trendy idea to entertain children rather than to enhance their education. But enhance their education it does - and in a way that more usual school equipment can only aspire to.

The importance of the sensory curriculum, particularly in schools for children with severe learning difficulties, cannot be over stated. As increasingly our schools are experiencing a growth in the number of children with profound and multiple learning difficulties as well as other complex needs, the importance of sensory work within the school's core curriculum increases.

It is easy to become complacent about the sensory needs of the child with severe learning difficulties. It is vital that we constantly ask ourselves as workers in the field of learning difficulties - what is it like for the child who has such difficulties? We need to remind ourselves that our environment and the events taking place within our bodies are experienced by way of special sense organs. The ear and the eye are obvious but so frequently taken for granted by the hearing and sighted who have had vast sensory experience and so automatically react often in the unthinking manner to visual and auditory stimuli. The tongue as the organ of taste, the skin as the organ of touch and the nose as the organ of smell are also well understood. We take much more for granted as sensory interpretations as part of all our daily lives. We need to remind ourselves when working with the SLD child (and the PMLD child in particular) that sensory impressions mediated by particular organs can vary in intensity and quality. We need to remember that the sensory impressions we are continually experiencing are rarely received in isolation but rather as a combination of sensory impressions which are then usually accompanied by a interpretation which is based on previously learned and experience behaviour - hence that ability to perceive and make sense of the world around us. But what of the child with severe learning disabilities? What freedom of choice does such a child have regarding sensory impressions? How do they interpret their own sensory activity? Do they have an adequate base of previous learning and experience upon which to build?

It is without doubt that the child with severe learning difficulties requires access to a sensory curriculum that is a part of a overall school curriculum. The more profound the learning difficulty the more sensory the curricular approach needs to be in order to develop cognitive and social skills. The sensory curriculum should be seen as one of the ways to aid development and so help the child make sense of the world around him/her and so move to becoming a more active and successful participant within it.

One of the most difficult concepts within Snoezelen for the teacher is that of 'passive' stimulation. As teachers, we are prone to 'force' intervention to simply facilitate. The very word intervention conjures up the notion of assertive direction to most teachers. Such a model is not always helpful and can in some cases be counter productive. We all know that children learn best when interested and their enthusiasm is built upon. With these points in mind, the staff have become aware of the need to employ the passive approach to sensory stimulation advocated by Snoezelen as much as possible. We very much felt that it was important to employ the full Snoezelen philosophy when using the dedicated Snoezelen room. Upon reflection, we realised that for many years, we had been operating a variety of programmes that provided passive sensory stimulation as well as opportunities for the children to control as many of their experiences as possible, though this did lack the clear philosophical base as expressed by Snoezelen. Activities were (and still are) provided for the children to experience their environment through their senses. Most of our PMLD pupils are unable to freely and fully explore their environment. Those that are more able to explore will often need additional help to learn to listen, look, feel and relax. Many of the children do, however, appear to have a preferred sense that staff have to become aware of, and utilise as a base upon which to develop other sensory experiences. Hazel, for instance, appears to enjoy looking and making contact with material introduced within her surroundings, whilst David seems to look more carefully at bright shiny objects, Samantha likes physical contact and 'happy' voices. It is often in this way of concentrating on what appears to be the child's strongest sense that work is carried out in a passive manner to develop responses across all the other senses. The Snoezelen room has obviously proved to be invaluable in providing a resource that is exciting and enormously stimulating to the children and that is controllable. By controlling the equipment set-up and operation in the room, a variety of different environments can be created that allows the child's preferences to be reflected. It is often when the child is relaxed and in the environment that they prefer that we are able to passively intervene with an activity of minor environmental change, that the child more readily accepts because it is non-threatening and non-demanding. Although it may be fun, we feel that the Snoezelen room we have is too valuable a resource to simply let the children loose in without some form of staff planning and control. To allow the children to get the most out of the facility, careful preparation based on clear aims and objectives need to be established by the teacher for each child. The following sheet is used by staff. As can be seen the teacher has to plan and quantify 'free' play and so view such as a part of a learning programme. Planning does not mean we are over prescriptive in the use of the Snoezelen facility, but it does allow us to see that the children get the most they can out of any Snoezelen session in terms of learning and enjoyment.

Whilst purposeful and controlled use of the senses can be developed by creating environments in which carefully planned sensory stimulation is available, it is important to record such so as to measure progress and enjoyment. We have employed a number of methods of recording - each of which has its own merits. Photographs can be taken of activities and the reactions of the participants. Video recording, although sometimes problematical, in low light conditions, is exceptional for recording movement and also has the added advantage of sound track. Written observations are very valuable providing they are made as near in time to the activity as possible. Checklist and tick box charts are good for rapid recording whilst actually interacting with a child. We have found it crucial to prepare for, and keep records of, Snoezelen sessions in order to monitor child progress, experiences and preferences. The keeping of good information also aids in the rapid setting up of a session based upon a child's individual needs and preferences. (Soft play - Snoezelen Observation sheet).

As staff, we decided to spend some time considering how best to present such an exciting resource to our children. We knew that the experience that the Snoezelen room had to offer would be new to most of our children and staff.

Through discussion and some clearly enjoyable hands on experience, it was decided to carefully record the first responses of each child using the 'Baseline Response to Snoezelen Equipment'.

We also decided that it would be useful to video some of the children to demonstrate the qualitative aspects of their experiences to others. This initial response work took a number of weeks and was very intensive of staff time as often one staff member was needed to observe and record while another interacted with the individual child. The interactive staff members was not there to engage the child in an activity as such but was needed to reassure some children during periods of minimum lighting or to assist the non-ambulant child in turning if they appeared to be unable to carry out an intended move. We also thought we might need additional support for our severe challenging behaviour children to restrain them from damaging the room and its electronics - this in fact proved unnecessary. All the staff time was thought to be worthwhile as it allowed for objective observation. The stimuli were not necessarily presented in the order on the baseline response sheet. After children had spent some time in the Snoezelen room, many teachers began to record a child' response to combination of stimulus presented simultaneously. The results of this information gathering exercise were interesting and varied. An example of a particularly pleasing first response was that of a boy of eleven. Due to a progressive metabolic condition, he has extremely limited movements and most communication takes place by accepting a long blink as a negative response and eye pointing as positive. Recently this has not always been clear, but the staff have continued to reinforce it by offering choices at every opportunity and honouring the slightest indication given of a negative or positive response. However, as can be seen on the baseline response sheet, Stephen made his choices in the Snoezelen room quite clear. The bubble units have continued to appear to be his most favourite piece of equipment.

Our Snoezelen room is a complete and self contained environment that can be used at short notice, and at the flick of switches provide a variety of sounds, smells, colours, light, tactile and knaesthetic sesations. It is a resource that is appropriate for all ages within the school and has the potential, as we are constantly discovering, of meeting a variety of needs. Whilst its application to the PMLD child appears quite clear, we must not forget that the rest of the SLD population is also able to benefit from the use of the sensory environment. The Snoezelen room has much to offer when working with sound, light and colour. We have found it a great resource for science when working with light and sound. With the use of the voice activated light panel and amplified speech, it has proved to have language development uses also. It has also proved extremely useful in calming distressed and disruptive children. Those children we have who exhibit severely challenging behaviour often find the room relaxing and non-threatening. We have noticed how their behaviour calms rapidly in the subdues soft lighting with wafting seductive music playing and the relaxing visual impact of the bubble tubes working. It is at such times that these children will allow extremely close physical contact and demonstrate clearly relaxed interactions with staff members. For some, the calmness of the room afforded us the opportunity to introduce them to aromatherapy and massage. Delivering such an experience whilst the child felt calm and safe in a non-demanding situation proved to be the start of a generalisation of the acceptance of aromatherapy and massage in other situations.

The providing of a dedicated Snoezelen room although not particularly costly, is a major budget commitment. The dedicated room also has the disadvantage of not being mobile. Children have to move to it and use the facility with equipment that is in the main permanently positioned within the room. Whilst we would never wish to be without our Snoezelen room, we rapidly became aware of the need to use pieces of Snoezelen equipment in classroom and the school hall. By using portable pieces of Snoezelen equipment, we have been able to create mini Snoezelen environments within classrooms and other teaching acres of the school. A corner of a classroom divided off with a parachute, for example, creating an area of low light intensity, becomes a very good basis for the creation of a mini Snoezelen. With the use of a few unbreakable mirrors, a single bubble tube, some soft furnishing and a tape player, we are able to create an environment within a matter of minutes that is both relaxing and enjoyable to be in. When our children are in such mini environments, the teacher, can then look to working on sensory issues or simply use the environment as a place that is conducive to the child becoming more receptive to other areas of curricular work. Such mini environments have proved extremely useful for the whole age and ability range within the school. The reading of a story certainly seems to be enhanced for the child when a group are sat within a mini environment. Mini environments can be easily changed and created in different formats and in different areas thus adding to variety for the children and staff. They are also relatively cheap to create.

Group work has been enjoyed by staff and children when mini environments have been created within classrooms or the school hall. These have sometimes been developed using particular themes such as 'the seaside' when most of the materials for sensory stimulation have corresponding qualities - seaside songs to move to; sand; shells, water, wind to feel; the sounds of the seas and gulls to listen to; wall displays and mobiles depicting seaside items and activities; photographs and colour slides of the seaside and family trips etc. This can then all be tied together with appropriate outings. In fact, the sensory work becomes the preparation for the outing and clearly builds the child's awareness to hopefully make the eventual trip more meaningful.

Whilst Snoezelen equipment is often used to create or enhance mini environments, it is possible to create an environment with little or no Snoezelen equipment but still work within it using the basic Snoezelen philosophy of passive learning. The use of dedicated Snoezelen equipment, however, does much to enhance any environment being created. To understand the need to enhance environments to support learning experiences, one only has to think of the occasions when you have perhaps wanted to listen to a favourite piece of music at home. You may have enhanced the environment to create an atmosphere that was conductive to sitting and listening to the particular piece of music. You may have subdued the lighting if late evening, and possibly had a fire or source of light that conveyed a feeling of warmth. You might then have had a glass of wine. All these things go to create an environment and atmosphere that gives a general feeling of well being upon which the enjoyment of listening to the music is enhanced. Such action of enhancing environments linked to activities works for us so why not use it in the classroom with children?

At Limington House, we often create mini Snoezelen environments in classrooms using portable equipment. Dividing an area of the room with draped material of parachutes gives a clearly defined area which itself becomes enticing to children. Snoezelen does not have to be based on the dedicated Snoezelen room. Whilst such a room is a tremendous asset, Snoezelen can be developed in a school relatively cheaply by using a few portable pieces of equipment to create mini environments in classrooms. Snoezelen is not simply about the equipment - it is about the philosophy of using the environment to create sensory experiences from which pleasure and learning can come.

We use Snoezelen and more particularly our dedicated room to enhance our sensory work and also to aid development in other curricular areas. It has proved successful for us in calming children when upset or undergoing periods of behaviour disturbance. It has been used extremely successfully in working with children to develop their exploration of the immediate environment - especially when encouraging them to reach out and simply touch a piece of equipment. This rapidly develops into a desire to control equipment and the effects created. It has been invaluable in working with auditory and visual location with children rapidly learning to turn and move towards a variety of sound and light sources. Kinaesthetic activities have been greatly enhanced by using equipment that vibrates or moves and so gives children direct movement experiences. The greatest effect of Snoezelen upon our children has been that of a build in self esteem and motivation. Whilst much of our evidence here is anecdotal, we have noticed how many children are more motivated to interact within the Snoezelen environment with others as well as the equipment. Interaction becomes more positive and clearly more enjoyable. It is indeed most satisfying to see behaviours learned or modified that appear to generalise to other areas of school life.

We continue to learn each day of ways to use Snoezelen and so aid the development and education of our children. This very versatile resource has much to offer that can only be fully appreciated by first hand experience of the philosophy and equipment used. We have even found it of use in delivering aspects of the National Curriculum - particularly for those working within level 1. It provides an exciting tool that can be used to enhance many areas of the special school curriculum. Record sheets are used by staff when using the Snoezelen and soft play rooms to support curricular work with pupils.

The Snoezelen room offers a safe environment where skills can be developed and transferred to the classroom setting, a place where a trusting and relaxing relationship can develop between child and carer. It is clearly a resource available to all ages and all abilities.

# A STUDY IN THE USE AND IMPLICATIONS OF THE SNOEZELEN RESOURCE AT LIMINGTON HOUSE SCHOOL

**Andrea de Bunsen**

## INTRODUCTION

For the first few years of a child's life, it is accepted that there is a great dependence upon others, but as children grow up they are encouraged to be independent and due time eventually achieve self sufficiency and independence, to the point of leaving the family unit and making their own major decisions. In the case of disabled individuals and those with challenging behaviour, the situation is maybe somewhat different. Serpell-Morris (1982) suggest that, "These children are very rarely going to take complete responsibility for their lives. They are always going to be in the care of one responsible adult or another ...." This fact accepts, therefore, the importance and the influence vested in those who are involved with disabled individuals and their lives. Serpell-Morris (1982) goes on to say that ".... you can never evade the fact that when you say "he needs", it was your judgement; you've got to take responsibility for that judgement".

The decision to study a group of pupils with challenging behaviour stems from my involvement with these pupils. The school, being the only one in Hampshire that has boarding provision for pupils with severe learning difficulties (SLD), accepts a greater ratio of students who display challenging behaviour. These pupils have often been excluded from other SLD schools in the county and for what-ever reasons, the parents are no longer able to cope with their offspring living at home. Although I teach a class of six pupils with extreme behaviour difficulties, often self abusive or violent to others, there are several more pupils in the school who display challenging behaviour at times during the day.

In January 1992 the school Snoezelen and also soft play room was opened. Snoezelen is a Dutch word meaning a combination of doze and smell. The Snoezelen concept was devised in Holland as a sensory input and leisure activity for people with severe disabilities and seeks to produce an amalgam of sensations and encourage relaxation. It is a white room often padded, with equipment such as fibre optic, bubble tubes, fans, projectors and uses aromatherapy and music. A pleasant atmosphere and a feeling of security is essential to the concept of Snoezelen. This is created in part by the environment but is also influenced directly by the abilities and attitudes of staff and helpers.

The use of the Snoezelen at this present time is, in my opinion, unsatisfactory. I feel that there is little direction on how to use the equipment and building appropriately, insufficient training for people like myself who hold the responsibility for the Snoezelen and inadequate use of the facility by the pupils. This has implications in itself for as previously stated, it is the staff who generally make the decisions for the students.

## AIMS

1   To investigate how the sensory stimulation facility (Snoezelen) at Limington House School is currently being used.
2   To research the effect of the Snoezelen facility on six pupils from across the school who display extreme challenging behaviour.
3   To evaluate and report on the findings of the research activities.
4   To put forward recommendations for further development of the Snoezelen resource.
5   To identify a consistent, cohesive programme for pupils with challenging behaviour which will assist the pupils and the management of those pupils in the school.

## BACKGROUND

Limington House School is one of the 10 Severe Learning Difficulties (SLD) schools in Hampshire. The 95 pupils are ranged by a combination of age, mental ability, physical ability and temperament. The school has termly boarding provision for 20 pupils, the majority of whom are older students. There is an impressive range of facilities at the school, including a hydrotherapy pool, a purpose built multi-sensory building (Snoezelen) as well as the usual aids for people with disabilities.

The school employs 12 teachers, 25 assistance with the rest of the 76 staff employed across the disciplines of all aspects of caring and administration. The challenging behaviour group was set up when the influx of pupils with challenging behaviour became evident and the behaviours affected the educational progress of both themselves and other in their peer group. Three of the boys are currently receiving medication in connection with their behaviour. Of the six boys in this group 5 have boarding provision at the school and the remaining 1 lives in a Social Services home. The behaviours exhibited by these pupils range from self abuse, such as head banging and/or biting to violent outbursts of kicking and punching staff, destroying equipment and attacking other children. Equally, they can be disruptive in the structured environment of a classroom setting, through attention seeking, low concentration and application levels and manipulation of peers. It is pertinent to note that when these pupils are left on their own, with only minimal adult intervention, the incidences of challenging behaviour are reduced.

## PLANNING

My intention was to evaluate the use of the Snoezelen after one year of use (Appendix A) and discuss its appropriateness in the curriculum. Whilst the responses back were somewhat predictable, they showed the advantage of such a facility, but highlighted the need for an awareness raising session to re-establish its intended use. This is mentioned now because subsequent planning and investigation meant that there would no longer be the time to explore that area more fully.

To raise awareness and improve motivation by proactive use of the Snoezelen, I decided to select 2 pupils from my class as they are clearly identified as having challenging behaviour and then take 4 pupils across the age range from the rest of the school. These pupils, though younger, also displayed the same behaviours described earlier and warrant higher staffing ratios. This would involve a wider audience of staff hopefully raising the profile of the Snoezelen as a resource to support the curriculum and also meet the needs of a group of pupils that often present difficulties for the staff and other pupils. This I felt would support both the research questions.

When approached, the staff were fully prepared to assist in the investigation of the effect of the Snoezelen on the pupils with challenging behaviour, although some of the staff were very sceptical of the programme's suitability and value. Comments such as, "I'm dubious that it will make any change", "I don't think that daily Snoezelen sessions will help a challenging behaviour pupil" (Appendix) and "All this is doing is confusing the child" (Appendix) imply a somewhat negative approach in dealing effectively with the type of pupils studied here. Booth and Pym (1982) said, "It must be remembered it very often rests on personalities. You can lead a horse to water but you cannot make it drink. There will be a number of persons in to be influenced, to be persuaded to adopt a different approach".

Although some staff were doubtful in their initial thoughts of the value of the Snoezelen for the study group, they all approached the task with a professional attitude and co-operation.

The first recording sheets (Appendix) was designed to show any regularities/irregularities in patterns and degrees of behaviour. I was concerned, however, that there was insufficient specific detail to help me with my research question, so I contacted Roger Norgate, the senior educational psychologist for Hampshire and after discussion, we devised a time sampling recording sheet (Appendix) which would better describe the behaviours of the pupils in the study. The original plan was to run a 4 week programme of 2 weeks without Snoezelen, 2 weeks with Snoezelen and then 2 weeks without Snoezelen. That way any changes in behaviour, either positive or negative could be observed in the middle section, and a subsequent reverting back to original behaviours could also be noted.

## METHODS OF INVESTIGATION

The following methods of investigation were used in this study:

*     Observing, assessing and working with the 6 pupils with challenging behaviour in the Snoezelen. The staff were instructed by myself as to how the pupils were to be managed in the Snoezelen. This involved massage, eye contact, quiet talking and generally building up a rapport in a quiet manner which will hopefully encourage the pupils to learn and develop the skill of relaxation. The Snoezelen provides an environment conducive to start this process.

*     Comprehensive records of staff observations and pupils' behaviour in the Snoezelen and of the change in behaviour over the 6 week research. The class teacher and the assistant who would be working with the pupil were asked to devise the 5 criteria for the weekly record sheets and to decide upon the number and nature of points for the time sampling records for their particular student. The sheets needed to be personal and meaningful to the staff operating them for the results to be significant.

*     Summaries of questionnaires with the staff working directly with each of the pupils, both before the research and afterwards.

*     Summary of taped interview with Christine Starr, aromatherapist and director of Holistic Therapy Centre, Plymouth. The concept of holistic therapy incorporates the medical, emotional and religious influences as one, eliminating the use of drugs to control behaviours. Christine is a native German speaker therefore her English is not idiomatic or grammatically correct on occasion.

*     Summary of a taped interview with Sally Oakley, Special Schools Assistant working with a pupil during this study.

*     Video of pupils in the Snoezelen and in the school environment. The video is complete but I was informed that the Open University discourages accompanying videos. Therefore, the tape has not been submitted.

* Conversations with Roger Norgate, Senior Educational Psychologist, Hampshire. Roger is currently writing the Hampshire policy document on the identification and management of challenging behaviour.

* Interviews arranged with Carol Goddard, Inspector for Special Needs, Hampshire and Pam Ottley, Educational Psychologist with immediate involvement with Limington House School. Both Carol Goddard and Pam Ottley cancelled their appointments due to illness and time did not allow an alternative date.

* Reading of relevant literature, although it must be stressed that there is very little information on Snoezelen, and even less on its use in education. The Snoezelen concept is very new and it seems no investigation studies on Snoezelen and challenging behaviour have so far been carried out.

## INFLUENCING FACTORS

There were several factors which influenced and affected the study. It was very difficult to gain an objective assessment of the pupils's behaviour, particularly as I was not directly involved in the recording sheets. One adult had been allocated to each pupil taking part in the study during school hours but the score on the weekly recording sheets (Appendix) were filled in by as many as 3 people over a 24 hours period and their interpretations of the behaviours would directly affect the scores on the sheets. The change to the time sampling sheet (Appendix) where only 1 staff member was recording made a true assessment easier. This meant that only 1 person accompanied and recorded the pupil in the Snoezelen and completed the time sampling sheets.

During the 6 week period, there were 2 staff and 1 pupil absent with illness for a number of days and 1 pupil's routine was disrupted with hospitalisation for 2 days, and 1 pupil was in the process of having medication, which was administered to sedate his behaviour. One of the pupils, had respite care during the period, and the challenging behaviour is always exacerbated at this time.

There were other factors which may have influenced the results, for example:

i) Christopher expected to go home one weekend and did not. His behaviour was poor for the 2 days where normally he would have registered reasonable behaviour.

ii) Supply staff in a class

iii)    Poor weather and consequent prolonged indoor play

iv)    Particular activities

v)    Who the pupil has to sit next to

vi)    Our misunderstanding of the pupils needs at certain times.

All these require further consideration and more in depth study than I have allowed but such factors are unavoidable: children cannot be studied in laboratory conditions.

The problems of accessing relevant literature have already been mentioned as has the difficulties of meeting with people outside of the school. The research questions and activities became increasingly large projects to undertake in the time frame and it is now evident that six pupils were too many to study in great detail, as the recordings and findings show.

## FINDINGS

It is evident from the replies from the questionnaire (Appendix) that the novelty of a new resource has diminished and there are aversive tendencies in the use of the Snoezelen. "I did have reservations as in the past he has not particularly enjoyed or appeared to have reaped much benefit from our usual timetabled period in the Snoezelen room". (Appendix Questionnaire). This study seems, from the follow up questionnaire, to have inculcated a more confident and assertive disposition partly due to a sense of being part of a team that had a direction which over the trial weeks negated any previous resistance. This new interest and enthusiasm was assisted with the response of the pupils when using the Snoezelen. All the staff noted that the pupils did not display negative behaviours while in the Snoezelen and began to relax and enjoy the time and contact with their respective adult. In turn, this positive feedback reflected in a new staff attitude. "I felt the study to be an interesting, worthwhile and potentially very useful .... He certainly seemed to enjoy the one to one attention and following the sessions in the Snoezelen he was more settled in the class". (Appendix Questionnaire 2). The improvements described by the staff are part way supported by statistical evidence formulated from the recording sheets. When dealing with people though, statistics should be used cautiously "A statistic can't measure a smile. A statistic can't measure this moment when they lie there and are just themselves". (Appendix). The statement is not entirely accurate but the sentiment has merit. The Pie Charts were formulated from the evidence from the weekly recording sheets (Appendix). The figures were taken from the recording sheets and put into a table of how many of each criteria number there were for each of the six weeks. Using Harvard Graphics these were then transfigured into percentages and presented as Pie charts, six for each pupil offering information each week.

With all but Stuart, who was ill, the pupils' Pie charts indicate varying degrees of behavioural improvement. This is particularly noticeable with Ian's and Christopher's. Though I had hoped for a more conclusive and clearly defined result the staff and I feel there are sufficient favourable indications to warrant further investigation.

The other important factor that emerged from the Pie charts was that in fact the pupils were good or reasonable for a vast proportion of the time during the week. These periods had been overshadowed by the shorter spells of challenging behaviour. Hopefully with the overall view, the Pie charts presented our perceptions of these pupils will alter and we can acknowledge the good instead of emphasising the bad. Our attitudes are probably a strong influence factor that needs further consideration. The Time Sampling Recording Sheet results were taken and plotted into histogram form and do show that during the middle two weeks while the pupil was using the Snoezelen, there was a reduction in the behaviours that the staff wished to reduce or eliminate. One slight deviance shows on Nicholas' histogram. The staff listed eye contact on his time sampling record sheets. Where other behaviours were considered negative and did reduce, the eye contact which they wished to improve did in fact increase. I am aware of the possibility of coincidence especially over such a short period of observation time but with the results of both recording sheets combined with comments from the staff and discussions amongst themselves, it would seem that this study would be worth continuing over a longer period. If our younger pupils with challenging behaviour could be helped before their physical size became a daunting additional difficulty, we are averting potential future problems. Prevention rather than cure!

## RECOMMENDATIONS

1    INSET TRAINING FOR ALL STAFF

    a)        In the use of the Snoezelen resource
    b)        To give advice and support when working with
              challenging behaviour pupils
    c)        Developing a sensory curriculum
    d)        To be able to understand a differential curriculum

2    Continuation of the recoding sheets to monitor all pupils with difficult or
     challenging behaviour accompanied with observation notes. Over a period of

time, we may see a pattern of frequency.

3     Continuation for certain pupils in using the Snoezelen daily.

4     That we must acknowledge good behaviour in "bad kids"

5     To introduce some the Snoezelen practices into the classroom and possibly the boarding provision and, the students homes.


## CONCLUSIONS

The Snoezelen is a valuable and worthwhile resource not only as a leisure activity for which it was originally designed, but for using its environment as an aid for attempting to be proactive in offering good positive programming. This will contribute to the pupils repertoire of skills particularly in the ability of relaxation and allow pupils and staff the chance to repair damage to relationships and enjoy one to one time with no pressure.

A behaviour is not intrinsically undesirable but is dependent on the values of others making the judgement. As stated in the introduction, we make judgements on behalf of our pupils so we must take responsibility for our decisions. Ethically, the least intrusive techniques raises fewer moral issues, though restrain procedures may be necessary in crisis situations. If the pupils crisis situations could be diminished by teaching them other skills to cope with or replace the behaviour we deem threatening then the moments of crisis will also diminish. The calming effect offered by such an environment as a Snoezelen room is possibly an alternative to break a negative chain of events. "Relaxing made a positive start, we are now ready for the day". (Appendix).

This study highlighted for me my role and responsibility. There are indications that the Snoezelen room used with positive planning becomes a neutral new environment and seems to result in a reduction in challenging behaviour. It is import to capitalise upon this effect through more effective and imaginative use of timetabling the room, utilising the concepts of relaxation techniques, massage and Snoezelen in other environments.

Though this study has left many questions unanswered, I feel encouraged despite their initial reservations, by the commitment, of the staff and by their contribution and teamwork. I am not advocating that the Snoezelen resource is the answer on its own but it could be instrumental if applied and exploited as a medium in a positive programme of management and as an educational resource.

**REFERENCES**

Bell J. "Doing Your Research Project" (1989) OUR Press

Booth T & Pym C. "Some Aspects of Special Education in Oxfordshire: Innovation and Change" in Booth T and Statham J (1982) "The Nature of Special Education" OUR Press

Hutchinson R. "The Whittington Hall Snoezelen Project" (1991) North Derbyshire Health Authority

Lavigna G & Donnellan A "Alternative to Punishment - Solving Behavioural Problems with Non-Aversive Strategies" (1986) New York: Irvington Publishers Inc.

Serpell-Morris G "Minds of Their Own: One Teacher's Philosophy" in Booth T & Statham J (1982) "The Nature of Special Education" OUR Press.

## LIMINGTON HOUSE SCHOOL - SNOEZELEN QUESTIONNAIRE

A year has now passed since the Snoezelen room was opened. Children and Staff are now familiar with the area. The beginning of the New Year is perhaps a good time to review the facility, the timetable, the way the resources are used and to develop a set of guidelines that will improve the way that the environment is used in the future.

1    Do you feel your working knowledge of all the equipment is adequate and if not, what equipment would like further practice with?

2    If there anything about the equipment or layout in the Snoezelen you would like to change in anyway?

3    How often do you use the Snoezelen and would you like more or less time?

4    What is the ratio and typical number of Staff and Pupils who use the resource in one of your sessions?

5    Do you feel the reporting of pupil activities whilst using the Snoezelen are effective or have any value, and how would you change these procedures.

6    What benefits or criticisms do you see or have of the Snoezelen.


Thank you for filling in the questionnaire.

# INTRODUCTION TO LIMINGTON HOUSE SCHOOL

Limington House School is one of 10 Severe Learning Difficulties (SLD) Schools in Hampshire. The school employs 72 staff across the disciplines of teaching, assisting, caring and all aspects of administration and it currently has 86 pupils based on four sites. Whilst there are general guidelines for looking after and teaching SLD pupils, the school has always enjoyed a measure of autonomy in directing its own requirements with reference to the individual needs of its pupils.

The pupils are ranged by a combination of age, mental ability, physical ability and temperament. The school has attempted to emulate normal education as far as possible and there are three broad groups of primary, secondary and further education (FE) units, each with a Profound and Miltiple Learning Difficulties (PMLD) class. All the PMLD classes are at the main school site with the primary unit, challenging behaviour class and the lower secondary classes. The top secondary and lower FE classes are both located within a local secondary community school, where pupils attend daily.

The school has a termly boarding hostel for up to 20 pupils, although it is in the process of moving over to 52 week care. The hostel is mainly for those who present challenging behaviour and for those who parents find that they can no longer cope with their child living at home. There are an impressive range of facilities at the school including a private swimming pool for hydrotherapy, a purpose built multi-sensory building (Snoezelen), a proposed Jacuzzi as well as the usual aids for disabled people.

I am the deputy headteacher at Limington House School and teach a group of five pupils with challenging behaviour with the support of three special school assistants.

## The School Aims

The school aims are laid out in several documents and have evolved to accommodate some of the changes which have occurred. Indeed, the evolution will be an ongoing process particularly with the move to LMSS. The primary aims of the school are towards its pupils to enable them to increase their knowledge, experience and understanding. The school curriculum is programmed individually to enable each pupil to follow an educational plan in line with the National Curriculum as far as ability allows. Emphasis is placed on communication skills, social skills, basic numeracy and the development of like skills. The secondary aims are to enable the pupils to become active participants within the community.

## What is Snoezelen

Snoezelen is a Dutch word meaning a combination of doze and smell. The Snoezelen concept was devised in Holland as a sensory input for people with severe handicaps as a leisure activity but had not been developed further. It is a white room often padded, with equipment that can relax or stimulate people. For example, fibre optics, bubble tubes, fans, lighting, aromatherapy and music may be used.

There is very little written on Snoezelen as far as I know, no research in its uses within education.

## Aims of the Study

Limington House is in the process of numerous changes which place heavy demands on the staff. The introduction of the Sensory building and Snoezelen was a new concept and little support was offered to the staff in how to utilise this resource and why it could be beneficial for our pupils.

Snoezelen has now become one of my responsibilities within the school and I would like to be able to support and motivate others in its uses with the backup of research data and realistic practical suggestions. The two research activities will hopefully begin this process.

Results of activity one will produce an overall picture and offer the opportunity for myself and staff to reflect on our teaching and use of the Snoezelen.

Activity two focuses on one particular group within our school, pupils with aggressive challenging behaviour (A,C,B). The reason for choosing this group is that these pupils concern all our staff and I also teach a class of older pupils with challenging behaviour though the research will be across all age ranges and classes.

I would predict success in the proposed trials and this I feel will help staff develop a positive attitude towards the educational value of Snoezelen other than using it solely as an enjoyable leisure activity.

By using observation and hopefully 24 hour recording of behavioural patterns with a group of pupils with aggressive challenging behaviour for two weeks with no Snoezelen input followed by two weeks of daily morning input, I hope to show an improvement by comparing the two results and noting differences. A control group will also operate using the same recording sheets but they will have no Snoezelen input during the four weeks.

The staff and myself will then reflect on the results and analyse if any useful information can be gleaned from the data.

## SNOEZELEN RESEARCH PROJECT

### Research Questions

1   How are the Snoezelen Resources being employed in my school?

2   What impact is this having on the pupils?

### Research Activities

I propose to discuss with staff my intentions for this module and the reasons why I need their help and co-operation for this research.

### Activity One

### Preparation

1   Devise a questionnaire for the staff, parents, therapists.
2   Discuss with the staff to be interviewed.
3   Agree interview schedules.
4   Agree times for observation and video filming and possibly tape recording.

### Interviews/Questionnaires

1   I propose to ask the headteacher, all teaching staff, a selection of assistants, a selection of the parents, all therapists, to complete the questionnaire.

2   I propose to interview a selection of the teachers, assistants, parents, therapists, pupils. I am aware that I maybe unsuccessful in interviewing the pupils.

### Preparation

1   Devise criteria to monitor improvement or change.
2   Discuss with staff/parents/carers who are to be monitored.
3   Agree interview schedules with the staff of pupils being monitored.

## Interviews

1 Within one (1) week interview teachers of pupils involved and possibly assistants, using tape recording or written notes.
2 Observations.

## Time

1 Discuss with the staff involved for

    a)    interviews
    b)    observations
    c)    their need to question me.

2 Consideration to my assistance for the time I am out of my class.
3 The need to remain in the time frame.

## Recording Keeping

1 Daily recording sheet preferably 24 hours support from parents and carers.
2 Observations and written notes.
3 Video support.

## Purpose

The area I propose to look at for this module is the use of the Snoezelen and its effects on pupils described as having aggressive challenging behaviour.

Hopefully, this will help me in working with my own group and offer support, encouragement and practical help to the other staff in their search for new methods of helping their pupils with behavioural difficulties.

I anticipate that a number of the pupils will benefit, I propose to monitor behaviour in a selection of pupils with aggressive behaviour for two (2) weeks with no Snoezelen then two (2) weeks with daily Snoezelen input.

## Timetabling for collecting information

**Time:**

1    Consideration to the staff time in school and out of school hours.
2    Consideration to my assistants for the time I am out of class.

### Record Keeping

Interviews - Tape recorded/written
Questionnaire
Videos
Observation Notes
Recording Sheets

### Purpose

I believe that we have a valuable resource in our Snoezelen room and that it can be extended into the classroom. My concerns are its value being utilised for the benefits of our pupils. There has been little research on Snoezelen and even less on its use in education. Hopefully, this research will

a)    Support its use as a valuable resource.
b)    Help staff and pupils utilise its potential.
c)    Help me in preparation to take training sessions in the use of Snoezelen and the sensory curriculum.
d)    Pinpoint problems and concerns so that I can improve or advise on them.

### Activity Two:

### Action Plan

### Research Activity One

I will interview a range of key people regarding their perception of the usage and impact of Snoezelen related to individual pupils.

| Names of those involved: | Teachers |
| | Assistants |
| | Therapists |
| | Inspectors/Advisors |
| | Educational Psychologist |

| Preparation: | Dates and times |
| | Devising a schedule |

| How, When, Where: | Consider school organisation |
| | and convenient time for staff. |

| Record Keeping: | Field notes |
| | Interviews and summaries |

| Use of Activity: | To help focus on the impact of |
| | Snoezelen on individual pupils |
| | Teachers perceptions on the |
| | use of Snoezelen |
| | This should help me identify |
| | difficulties and offer support. |

## Research Activity Two

I will use a questionnaire with staff to discover usage and views of Snoezelen.

| Name of those involved: | Staff involved with study |

| Preparation: | I will prepare 2 questionnaires |
| | - 1 to be completed before the |
| | study commences, the second on |
| | completion. |

| How, Where, When: | Before/After study |
| | Convenience of staff |

| Record Keeping: | Questionnaire |
| | Observation notes |
| | Summary of taped interviews |

| Use of activity: | Identify difficulties and support staff and pupils |
|---|---|

## Research Activity Three

I will video pupils and staff in class and Snoezelen as part of my observations.

| Names of those involved: | Staff and Pupils (if they agree) taking part in the study |
|---|---|
| Preparation: | Arranging convenient dates and times<br>Booking Video Camera<br>Arranging for editing |
| How, When, Where: | Classroom, Snoezelen |
| Record Keeping: | Video tape<br>Observation comments |
| Use of activity: | To help support my findings<br>Offer focus and support to staff |

## Research Activity Four

Reading and information seeking through literature search, Special Needs Advisor, Educational Psychologist etc.

| Names of those involved: | King Alfreds College Library<br>Special Needs Adviser<br>Educational Psychologist |
|---|---|
| Preparation: | Arranging convenient dates and times |
| How, When, Where: | Winchester School<br>Dependant on others |
| Record Keeping: | Written notes<br>Materials |

| Use of Material: | Backup/support |
| | New perspective |

**Research Activity Five**

Observing and recording behaviours of study group of pupils before and after Snoezelen.

| Names of those involved: | Staff and pupils involved in study |

| Preparation: | Formulating recording sheets |
| | Observation practice |

| How, When, Where: | Using daily recording sheets |
| | Classroom/Snoezelen |
| | Staff, carers, parents |

| Record keeping: | Quick meaningful sheets |
| | Daily records |
| | Written back-up notes |

| Use of activity: | Base of material for study |
| | Body of study |
| | Relevant to pupils and staff |
| | Preparation for future actions |

**Week One**

1 Give out Questionnaire.
2 Interview selected staff for activity one.
3 Select pupils to be observed for activity two in consultation with staff.
4 Discuss recording methods with the staff in activity two.

**Week Two**

1 Monitor recording sheets (activity two) are being filled in.
2 Interview selected staff for activity two.
3 Begin observations and recording for activity one.

## Week Three

1     Monitor recording sheets for activity two are being filled in.
2     Continue observations and recording activity one.
3     Check preparation/timetable for daily morning sessions in Snoezelen for selected pupils, for weeks 4 and 5.
4     Classroom observations and videoing.

## Week Four

1     Timetabling morning sessions in the Snoezelen for the next two weeks.
2     Monitor recording sheets for activity one.
3     Observations in Snoezelen and classroom videoing.

## Week Five

As above for Week Four.

## Week Six

1     Check all recording sheets
2     Staff interviews and follow up
3     Write up observations
4     Discuss comparisons of the two week block in activity two with staff.

## INTERVIEW WITH SALLY OAKLEY, SPECIAL SCHOOL ASSISTANT - LIMINGTON HOUSE SCHOOL, 25 JANUARY 1993

### Before

*What did you think the study was about?*

I understood the study was to identify areas of challenging behaviour displayed by individual children, when, where and how often these behaviours were taking place and to ascertain whether a period of time in the Snoezelen room in any way alleviated these problems.

*What did you feel would be the outcome of the programme?*

The child I was looking after often arrived at School in a very agitated manner. I hoped that a period of time spent in the calm atmosphere of the Snoezelen would be beneficial to him although I did have reservations as in the past, he has not particularly enjoyed or appeared to have reaped much benefit from our usual timetabled period in the Snoezelen room.

*This project is for pupils with challenging behaviours, do you feel the daily Snoezelen would help?*

As mentioned above, our normal allocated time in the Snoezelen has been particularly successful in alleviating the child's behaviour. However, I think it would be interesting to observe Stuart's reaction during regular daily sessions instead of one hour once every other week. Stuart does not react well to changes in the environment and the fact that he would have the opportunity of becoming better acquainted and more familiar with the Snoezelen environment was a good opportunity for him.

*What difference in behaviour did you expect to see?*

I did have reservations as I already mentioned but I felt Stuart would definitely benefit from the opportunity presented to him.

*Prior to this project, describe the pupil's behaviour.*

As mentioned, Stuart didn't react very well at all to the change in environment and he takes a long time to settle down. He is usually very vocal in the Snoezelen but he tended to take the form of shouting rather than sound of enjoyment or interest. He would rarely settle to observe any particular area and would run from one end of the room to the other. I have never observed any interaction with other children in the class in the Snoezelen.

*Describe the pupil's equipment preferences.*

Stuart would spend a little time in the mirror and bubble area but was very restless and only remained sitting or prone for a very short time.

*What behaviours were displayed in the Snoezelen, ie, increased attention, vocalisation, etc, or any negative behaviours?*

Stuart's behaviour patterns, ie, saliva play, biting hand, shouting or crying are usually present in the Snoezelen. However, during the Snoezelen observation period, he was usually quiet and very content to sit with me and seemed to be taking more notice of the surroundings. However, it must be noted that Stuart was in fact unwell during the 2 weeks period and was displaying a similar pattern in class. However, he was certainly much calmer during the sessions and hopefully anticipated them with enjoyment, eg. he would pull at his shoe laces when I said that it was time to go to the Snoezelen.

*Describe the level of adult involvement in the Snoezelen?*

Normally, Stuart was reluctant to sit or lie with an adult in the Snoezelen room and paid scant attention to verbal or physical prompting by staff. However, as mentioned during the two week period of re-study, Stuart was content and would initiate contact with me, himself and would follow directions, eg "Look at the bubbles etc". Stuart did not, however, interact in any way with the other children in the Snoezelen.

*Outline any concerns you feel the project will have on your daily routine?*

I thought it might cause problems and confusion with the staffing in the classroom.

## INTERVIEW WITH SALLY OAKLEY, SPECIAL SCHOOL ASSISTANT - LIMINGTON HOUSE SCHOOL, 31 MARCH 1993

### AFTER

*What constraints and workloads did the study put on you?*

I felt the study to be an interesting, worthwhile and potentially very useful. We are very fortunate to have a Snoezelen facility in the School and should ensure every use is made of it. As most of our children arrive fairly promptly at 9.0'clock, I was able to assist the teaching in toileting etc before taking Stuart to the Snoezelen for his early morning session.

*Is it a feasible daily situation?*

Owing to the fact that the Snoezelen is in use for most of the school day, the early morning sessions would mean some reorganisation to allow for the children with challenging behaviours to have the opportunity for some individual time in the Snoezelen. Flexibility would be of paramount important as situations can arise which prevent adherence to a strict timetableing regime.

*Can you tell me of your daily experiences with this regime?*

I found taking part in this study a worthwhile experience and I had the opportunity of observing the reaction of other children in the school presenting challenging behaviour and the views of other staff taking part, as well as the opportunity of spending individual time with Stuart. It was difficult on occasions, for example, absence of the class teacher and supply staff to adhere strictly to the time element of the regime: and there was the obvious difficulties of leaving only one person coping with the rest of the class.

*Do you feel there have been any changes in behaviour?*

As mentioned, Stuart was unwell for part of the study. It is difficult to say how much the Snoezelen influenced Stuart's definitely improvement in behaviour, for example, less saliva play, decreases in shouting and hand play. he certainly seemed to enjoy the one to one attention and following the sessions in the Snoezelen, he was more settled in class and displayed less of his usual behaviour patterns.

*This was a short study, do you feel it should have been extended?*

I think an extended study would be useful particularly in the case of Stuart as it was difficult to make definite judgements of any benefits derived owing to his state of health during the study. I also feel that Stuart benefited from the opportunity of becoming more familiar with the Snoezelen environment.

*How did you feel about the study?*

A worthwhile study and a good opportunity to look at other children presenting challenging behaviour.

*What did you gain from the study?*

As I said before, "it was good". Within a mixed ability class, it is difficult to isolate individual problems at the time and concentrating on this aspect and recording details from observation periods helped to identify when and during which activities problems arose:

*What did your pupil gain from the study?*

I think Stuart enjoyed the individual time which the study allowed and gave him the opportunity of becoming more familiar with the Snoezelen environment.

*Has it changed your attitude to the Snoezelen?*

I would welcome the opportunity of taking part in further studies and feel the study could be extended to include other children in the school although the practical organisation aspect could be problematic.

*What other questions would you have asked?*

None.

*Any other comments?*

Observation periods could be extended to include more recording of behaviour following Snoezelen sessions.


## INTERVIEW WITH CHRISTINE STAR, SPECIAL SCHOOL AROMATHERAPIST & DIRECTOR OF THERAPY CENTRE - LIMINGTON HOUSE SCHOOL, 2 APRIL 1993

A: "... going out and doing something in the community eg: ice rink. We will do that as well".

C: "I would like to stress an important point, we have the tendency to bring these other activities on the children. Yes, it was fine to go on the ice rink, swimming pool, you are actually enabled people and allow people to be followed by quiet and to do full of value by nothing and we really lost this. We have this feeling we constantly need to make and do, and there is nothing else and receiving and enjoying. So the balance needs to be right as ever, breathing in, breathing, out giving and taking. These activities doing something out, being in the community. But of all this, doing nothing. Does this make you feel on your own? Or with this one person? I think it is wonderful that you have the ability now".

"I hope you can develop it further, a better variety with the course and the small verses Preston comes out on as if a mystic approach far more important. Some bits do not work for everyone, some people are going to respond more to different things. You do not want to be approached and bombarded with something what happened was the overall. Let them go out and fix it later.

"Yes we have to let each person in its speed initiate to the problem. There will be some of few staff that will be very much interested in this, they will take it on. You know you cannot have all twenty teachers sitting in the Snoezelen. There will be some outside affair. I don't think it is wrong for all people who are interested in the same things, but if only the half of the people I have seen today are encouraged to use much more touch and the oil, smell for the classroom, but or themselves too. Because they are getting much more strong into the class and can give this kind of balance quietness to the children. If only 50% of the children I have seen today take this on but take it that little bit further then it has been extremely satisfying and successful day".

**A:** "I hope you find it successful?"

**C:** "Oh, yes".

**A:**
"O.K. Its just that it was interesting to see how you'd feel about them if you think the approach is a good approach. There's obviously some staff that think, No, it's not going to help the children or change their behaviour. Obviously, its not on its own, its not going to change their behaviour on its own".

**C:** "The oil on its own does not help in any way. But I'm convinced that it is helpful to the better, it is such a brilliant concept. When I said I do not need statistics. In it there's a sort of object like I think it is silly have a statistic, because what can a statistic measure? A statistic can't measure a smile. A statistic can't measure this moment when they like there and just themselves. Even if I give them 20 minutes and their going out still aggressive but they have had the 20 minutes quiet here and happy. Then each time when you bring them in, in their DNA System, it creates something of happiness and one day they bring this happiness out there. Therefore you can't measure it in two weeks or in six weeks".

**A:** "No. It isn't long enough is it?"

**C:** "No. It need to be much more longer, but there is not the slightest doubt for me, benefit of this kind of Snoez room but all the being very much happier and active over near the site. I wish I would be a child, I could stay in here much more. (Ha, Ha).

**A:** "I think they definitely would. The majority of the teachers and a number of assistants have already shown an interest so there wouldn't be a problem with that at all. For their own personal use as well as to support they would like to actually increase in their ability to give to the children".

**C:**
"Yes, it is a two way thing. If I am not right, how would I give anything of right to the children?"

**A:** "Yes".

**C:** "I really need to, that the tendency is all the helpless. The "Helpless helper" we call them. They are constantly helping and helping and wearing themselves so much out, that they are so much ....".

**A:** "The can't ...."

**C:** "The helper has to look after him/herself to be nurtured, and fit and you know. Fat, fit and fat. The eating comes again".

**A:** "O.K. Thank you very much indeed for your help!"

# BALDERS HUS (THE HOUSE OF BALDER), THE OLD HOUSE WITH THE NEW IDEAS

**Marianne Melberg**
**Gunilla Jansson**

Balders hus is housed in the old building of craftsmen in NorrtNlje. The premises are spacious, light and newly renovated and centrally located by the bus station in NorrtNlje (Sweden).

In Balders hus there is a training school with two special classes where 7-10 pupils get their daily education. It also contains a Snoezelen centre with a number of special rooms for Snoezelen activities.

With these words we begin the report about Balders hus. How we first come into contact with the Snoezelen and why we chose to work in accordance with this method and how the process - the way there - has happened.

## The organisation

In Sweden there are two types of compulsory special schools, the special elementary school for pupils who can profit from theoretical education and the training school. The pupils of Balders hus are in the training school and form a special group because all of them have multiple handicaps.

In Sweden almost all special school regardless of type are integrated in ordinary elementary schools.

The training school of Balders hus, however, is not integrated in a school building, it is a separate unit.

The Care Committee of Stockholm County Council has the overriding responsibility for the special schools. However, a new law stimulates that on 1 January, 1996, at the latest, the responsibility for all special schools in Sweden shall be taken over by the municipalities.

The municipality in which Balders hus is located is the municipality of NorrHlje. The plan up to the present is that the municipality of NorrtHlje will take over on a contract basis from January 1994.

## How our Snoezelen ideas started

In May 1991 we made our first study tour to Solbo in Denmark after having seen, some months earlier, a videotape from the Snoezelen house in Solbo. We felt that what we saw and experienced in Denmark was really something we wanted to use in the work with our pupils with multiple handicaps. It was there the process began. We videotaped. We experienced Snoezelen with our senses. We discussed.

Back from the study tour we naturally reported to the rest of the school staff. The same staff now working with Snoezelen in Balders hus. The staff consists of two special teachers and four assistants to the pupils, who all have the proper education and have long experience of children, young people and adults with an intellectual disability and who are on an early level of development.

Shortly before we saw the videotape and heard of Snoezelen we had started using tactile stimulation in the work with our pupils. It was our way to stimulate/strengthen our pupils in their identify and comprehension of the body. We also think it is an excellent way to get contact and to work with communication. The method is a kind of touch massage, which is very constructive way of working. Maybe that is why we adopted it and understood that Snoezelen activities would be really valuable for our pupils. We also saw response, well-being and joy in our pupils as a result of the tactile-touch methodology.

We immediately wanted to start working in a more intentional and purposeful way with Snoezelen activities. What happened was that we who had made the study tour returned completely filled with Snoezelen, but this had the opposite effect. We had experienced, the rest of the staff had not. Later we understood that everyone has to experience with his whole body and all his senses Snoezelen activities to be able to understand the idea of Snoezelen methodology. We continued working with the small resources we had. For example, we hung textiles in the ceiling of the school hall, we decorated the walls with material stimulating to sight, hearing and touch.

During the term the idea came up to apply for a grant for the entire staff to make a study tour to the Snoezelen house in Solbo, Denmark. Money was granted and the whole staff went to Denmark in May 1992.

We had now reached step 2 on our "journey" to having our own Snoezelen activity. The whole staff now had with their own eyes and senses tried Snoezelen activities. Everybody was quite convinced that Snoezelen was right for our pupils.

*164*

Three weeks after the study tour to Denmark, we made another study tour, this time to Chesterfield in England. We got a grant from a teachers scholarship. In June 1992 we visited Whittington Hall Hospital.

This journey became completely decisive in the future planning and creation of Balders hus thanks to the fantastic Snoezelen Centre of Whittington Hall Hospital and our host's experience and skill in this area.

We felt further strengthened and now wanted to work more concretely in order to give our pupils Snoezelen stimulation in our own way and from the new and old experiences that we had.

## Our previous experiences

In the last 10-15 years research and new methods concerning intellectually disabled people have developed. We want to mention some people who have been important to our way of working.

Lillie Nielsen - a Danish Sight Pedagogue. Her methodology is based on an overall view, in which the child emotional, motorial and social development are connected. Lillie Nielsen divides her methodology in five different phases. Offering technique, Imitation, Interaction, Distribution of work and Consequence technique. Many elaborate aids are part of the "methodology". She has for example published some booklets "Grab and you can grasp" (1977) and "on the way to a methodology" (1978).

Paiget - with the different phases of development, the sensory motorial period which lasts from birth to the age of 2 in a persons development. It is the phase in which most of our pupils are in their development.

Jean Ayres - who wrote the book "Interaction of the senses" (1979). In the book she describes the sensory integration, which organises and co-ordinates different sense impressions from the surrounding world.

Gunnar Aylen
- senior lecturer, who has carried on psychological and pedagogical research on intellectual disability.

Many other pedagogues and research workers, through the years, have published reports and method plans about communication and comprehension of reality and so on, which of course have been important for the development of the work.

## We found the house

We were shown the big building, which was to become Balders hus shortly after our return from England in June 1992. We had had to move out of the premises we were then housed in.

When we came into the house we saw the possibilities. It resembled Whittington Hall Hospital. Old on the outside - fantastic on the inside. It was big and had a high ceiling. The 320 m² we were offered were only meant to be a temporary arrangement for one term. The building was then to be pulled down. The first floor in this fantastic house was ours. The house had stood there a long time. It was once the house of the craftsmen in NorrtHlje, but there had also been many other activities in it: vocational school, audio-video centre, carpentry shop, sewing shop and assembly-rooms. Many people have attended weddings and other festivities here. The parquet floor of oak wood, which we found beneath many layers of carpets indicated this. At the opening on the 18th of May 1993 the head of the municipality told us about different festivities he had taken part in in our house.

Two weeks before the beginning of the term in August 1992 the staff started work in the premises. We set out the furniture we had brought from the premises we had left and unpacked our school equipment. At first it was rather empty in these enormous rooms. Two carpenters became our work-mates for two terms. None of the staff is very good with technical things. We got into contact with a man who has no technical education, but who is skilled at almost everything. We gave him the ideas, he pondered and when ready it turned out as we had planned. As our financial resources were limited we engaged small local firms in around NorrtHlje for our Snoezelen material. The response was very positive. They all did there very best, furthermore we have a head who trusts us and ventured upon the enterprise of creating Balders hus.

There was hammering and nailing, drilling and polishing. When the autumn term was over and it was Christmas most of the rough work was done. The walls were raised, most of the electrical wiring was done and most of the painting was finished. There had been lots of work done during the term. There were not only visible results, but also other results like many discussions, thoughts and ideas.

As long as the pupils were at school during the days our attention were on them and their activities. We worked late many afternoons and evenings. It was necessary to get everything in order.

Our head had negotiations with the municipal authorities about a prolongation of the lease and finally managed to get a few years. We hope now that there will never be a decision to demolish the building.

The school and the Snoezelen "centre" were beginning to take shape. After well deserved Christmas holidays the work continued. We felt the atmosphere in the house. We had a couple of wall paintings and contrast paintings done by a female painter in the municipality.

From our study tour in Denmark we brought back a song about a nightingale which we sing every morning. A whole wall was decorated by the artist with a landscape, trees and a nightingale. The Danish sight pedagogue Lillie Nielsen has created many aids for stimulation of children with multiple handicaps, among others a so called resonance plate made of plywood with an edge around it. The purpose is that the child shall lie on it and get feed-back from its own sounds. Hardly any motorial capability is necessary for the pupil to get response on this plate. The problem was that these resonance plates were always in the way. In Denmark we also got the idea to hang the plates on the wall when not in use. They shall of course be easy to take down for use. We let our artists make small works of art on the back of these plates, which now adorn a couple of the school walls.

At first the intention was to keep the school and the Snoezelen centre apart, but during the work the Snoezelen part has been integrated with the school. Let us say it has got the upper hand in a way which is positive for all of us. Every pupil now has Snoezelen activities on his schedule. After school hours everybody who for one reason or other needs to use the house is welcome.

Our opinion is that working with Snoezelen methods gives our pupils, visitors and ourselves a meaningful existence.

The training school has a statutory educational plan. It was last rewritten in 1991 with timetable, goals and general outlines. It stipulates that the pupils of the training school shall have education in the following subjects.

Communication and social interaction

Comprehension of reality and knowledge of the surrounding world

Creative activities

Motorial training

Training in daily living (ADL training)

All subjects join each other. The work with pupils on an early level of development must naturally be very concrete, here and now. In the subjects communication - tactile stimulation we work with clear and concrete signs, for example, immediately before lunch we place a spoon in the pupil's hand. When it is time to go bathing we give them their bathing-suite.

The staff use simple signs as an aid to speech, for example when you tell the pupil "you shall go out now" you also make the sign which means "go out".

## Comprehensive of reality and knowledge of the surrounding world

Comprehensive of room and time.

Give a possibility to investigate the room, to change position of the body, for example - stand, sit, lie under/upon, get experiences in different rooms/surroundings.

Tactile stimulation.

Make it possible for the pupil to establish time connections, help the pupil to get structure in life.

## Knowledge of quantity and quality

To give the pupil a possibility to feel - touch different matters for example water, colours, clay, to experience different kinds of substances.

**Cause, effect and expectance** are also included in this subject.

## Creative activities

Music and rhythm is a concrete working method. To offer creative activity to pupils on an early development level is to give many different sense experiences - stimulation.

**Motorial training** is training of movements, to get to know your own body and to move in different surroundings. Tactile stimulation is an example of motorial training for pupils on an early development level.

## Training in daily living

This comprises daily activities like dressing and undressing, hygiene, eating situations and social training suited to pupils own possibilities and conditions. Sense stimulation - Snoezelen methodology, which now has been integrated in the activities of the school day fits very well in the work with pupils on an early development level.

Snoezelen methodology gives many choices and activities for the pupils. Snoezelen methodology is a way to offer the pupil stimulation for the individual's own possibilities and conditions. It improves observation and the ability to concentrate. It builds up and strengthens reactions in a natural way. To work and to be able to offer surroundings, which are so tempting and worthy to explore, which give stimulation and experience, give the very best opportunities for development.

## Balders hus - school

Balders hus training school has room for 10 pupils. All the present pupils of the school have multiple handicaps ie besides their intellectual disability they have other disabilities, like defective vision, impaired hearing, autism or a physical disability.

Each day starts with a gathering when we sing the same songs every day. We sing among other things about the pupils, their names and what we shall do in school that day. The purpose of this gathering is that everyone shall be noticed - also the staff - and be acknowledged as an individual.

## Each day of the week has a main activity

| | | |
|---|---|---|
| Monday | - | music |
| Tuesday | - | creative activities |
| Wednesday- | | bathing |
| Thursday | - | gymnastics |
| Friday | - | training in daily living |

Besides the day's main activities every pupil has his own individual gymnastics programme.

All the pupils have Snoezelen on their schedule, which means that every pupil spends some time during the day in one of our Snoezelen rooms. Tactile stimulation is also a regular activity during the week.

We offer possibilities for stimulation by adapting the surroundings so they are as attractive as possible to our pupils and later in the day also to our Snoezelen visitors. In order to get to the training school you pass the corridor of the Snoezelen centre, which has a tactile touch wall and material stimulating to the eyesight.

The school premises consist of a big classroom of about 80 m2. It has a high ceiling and a big pillar in the middle. In one corner of the room a "shelf" has been built at an angle with mirrors on the wall, many big cushions in strong colours and a trellis hanging over each part. Many of our pupils who are dependent on a wheel-chair need to leave the chair to stretch out their bodies. Here, we can all be together, pupils as well as staff have a wonderful cosy corner. In the trellis you can hang many different materials stimulating both to eyesight and hearing. Eyesight lamps and spotlights have been put up in the ceiling and light the corner. A small portable fan is there to make breaths of wind to move and rustly paper hanging from the trellis. The floor-area is large, so there is also room for a hammock in with our cosy corner. In the room are a few oval tables where we have our morning gathering. A big mural painting adorns one wall in the classroom. It is a painting of a nightingale, of which we sing every morning. After the big room there are two smaller ones. One is about 18 m2 and is called the small classroom. The other is only 12 m2 and is used for tactile stimulation.

The kitchen is at the very back of the house. There we have the school lunch, which is an important time of the day. Our aim is to make it as calm and free from stress as possible and that every pupil shall be able to eat at his own pace.

### Balders hus - a Snoezelen centre

While we have built up the activity the local newspaper has written two reports. After these reports many day centres, residential group homes, staff working with children in pre-school age, organisations of parents, people who work with mentally disturbed people and families with children with multiple handicaps have phoned us to make an appointment for a study visit. During these visits we inform them of our activities and they can also try our Snoezelen rooms.

When writing this in November 1993 there are many people who rent the premises. It has become a problem to find a vacant time for everyone. An important task for us has been to inform staff who accompany the visitor of why and how to use the Snoezelen rooms. Every visitor is given a questionnaire on which the mind fills in how the visitor has reacted in the Snoezelen rooms. After about eight times we try to find out what affect the visits have had on the person and how we shall continue. We think it is important to work in periods and make recurrent assessments to avoid routine. We fear that it might otherwise become an aim in itself to take care of a person regardless of individual needs "from the cradle to the grave" as a saying goes here in Sweden.

Our pupil assistants are the ones who are responsible for and take care of the Snoezelen visitors. It has been like an advancement for them in their professional role. We now arrange courses on the subject: working with Snoezelen methods in Balders hus. The interest for these courses has been very great.

## Conclusion

This "journey" which we started about two years ago has been a process like all work to change things. The policy of Balders hus as regards the staff is that everyone on the staff regardless of professional title takes part in all activities with the pupils. Everyone is equally important. The process has been positive for staff and pupils. We have together made Balders hus what it is, a house full of the pleasure of working on many levels.

For the pupils there have been important changes. They have during the process had many new experiences. They have new and changed school premises and a Snoezelen centre with all that follows with it, adapted surroundings and methods.

For the staff the change has been equally important. We have during the process acquired new insight. We have learned a different way of working and furthermore we have go two new members of the team, two adult intellectually disabled girls who help us with the kitchen work and the cleaning of this house.

The basic views and attitudes of the staff of Balders hus -

- *      Positive treatment
- *      Everyone shall be seen
- *      Calm pace
- *      Accepted as I am
- *      Everyone works to his capacity and under his conditions
- *      Adapted surroundings

Our journey has been stimulating and is bearing fruit.

# SNOEZELEN - AN EVALUATION OF A SENSORY ENVIRONMENT USED BY PEOPLE WHO ARE ELDERLY AND CONFUSED

Leslie Pinkney
Paul Barker

## ABSTRACT

This chapter outlines the developments that have been made with the Snoezelen room at a centre for the Elderly with Mental Health problems. The chapter describes the selection of the equipment and its evaluation with relation to the Elderly with Confusional states and their carers. The staff training and development that was required and the approach, attitude and philosophy that was ultimately evolved. It also looks to the future and the way forward for Snoezelen with the Elderly with Mental Health problems.

## INTRODUCTION

Snoezelen with the Elderly is a relatively new idea which is slowly growing in this country. Although the principles are similar to the original concept, there has been some adaptation in the approach and the environment in order to meet the specific needs of the Elderly Mentally Confused person. This group of people lose the cognitive ability to assimilate information form their environment and their interpretations can often be seen as inappropriate and disorientated. Selecting activity for them can prove to be extremely frustrating for staff and relatives and requires skill, a high tolerance level and perseverance. For the moderately confused person there are the activities of Reality Orientation, Reminiscence Therapy and general activities of daily living encompassing social skills, vocational skills, kitchen and home skills, and maintenance of habits and routines. Despite this long list, Snoezelen can be appropriate on this group providing relaxation and an enjoyable environment that is totally failure free.

## DEVELOPMENT

The Snoezelen concept was first introduced to this client group two years ago following a search for an appropriate activity medium for the severely confused patients which yielded few ideas. It was recognised that we needed an activity that did not require any intellectual reasoning or a verbal response and could be used by staff, carers and relatives with minimal training. Initially, we were unsure of how we could implement this idea and were restricted to using the approaches designed with people with learning difficulties, but with familiarity, we were able to adapt the approach and the environment to suit our patients.

Before selecting a Snoezelen room within the hospital, we undertook a pilot study whereby we introduced three patients to a Snoezelen environment located within a locally based hospital unit for people with learning difficulties. This allowed us to evaluate the patients' response and consider the feasibility of introducing a similar environment. Following this trial period, we were able to design a room and implement our own approach specifically for the Elderly Confused. The final room design included some adaptations from the original room tested in the pilot study and although we were sure this was a good arrangement we made further changes as the research progressed. Figure 1 shows the original room design.

## Room Preparation

In order to maintain the highest level of reflection, the room was painted white. Although previous rooms have been painted this colour, there is experimentation going on using alternative colours to promote different feelings to the room. To prevent the room becoming too clinical, we used heavy curtains and pale drapes to soften the image, giving the room a cosy feeling which was more acceptable to the participants.

*Figure 1*

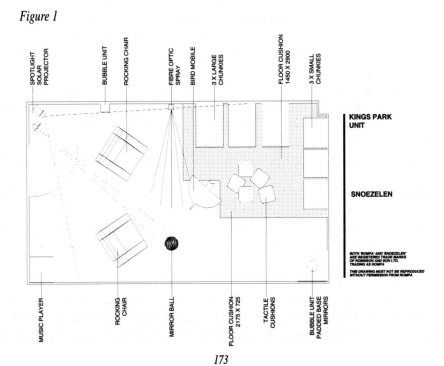

## Floor Covering

As many elderly people have problems with mobility, we chose to partially carpet the floor allowing for areas for seating as well as an area of soft floor covering. The carpet provided tactile stimulation while the soft cushioning and seating provided an element of choice.

## Seating

Seats were chosen for good ergonomic design and comfort. Rocking chairs provide an excellent opportunity for vestibular stimulation and are a good reminder of rocking chairs that they may have had at home. The large bean bag, although difficult to get out of, was also very successful. However, this could be used to maintain good positioning on the soft cushioning.

## The Equipment

The pieces of equipment selected for the room were chosen for their perceived suitability for a room for the elderly.

* Projector and Effect Wheels - Familiar projections were chosen for their reminiscent qualities and abstract projections for the eye catching colours. A prism was fitted to the projector to maximise the wall space by causing the image to circulate around all the four walls.

* Spot Light and Mirror Ball - These were proven to be popular in other rooms we visited and were instrumental in softening the edges of the room. The lighting produced from this piece of equipment encouraged gentle visual stimulation.

* Bubble Machine - This was chosen to fill the room with bubbles. Hand held bubble pots had been used with some of the severely confused elderly with great success and we had hoped to replicate this form of sensory stimulation. Reaching for the bubbles had encouraged visual tracking and fine finger movement.

* Optic Fibre Spray - This piece of equipment was chosen as a centre feature. The fine colourful strands provided a focal point while the flexible material they were made of was safe enough for 'hands on'

interaction. The equipment was accessible from both the floor and the chairs.

\* Bubble Unit - This was the only provider of olfactory stimulation. Oils were chosen for their familiar and reminiscent qualities, ie Lavender, or their relaxation properties, ie Ylang Ylang and Geranium.

\* Music - A selection of music formats were chosen. New age music was used as we had heard in previous Snoezelen rooms but we also tried more familiar and possibly reminiscent themes ie

| | |
|---|---|
| The Humming Chorus | Madam Butterfly (Puccine) |
| Ave Maria | (Gounod) |
| Nun's Chorus | Casanova (Strauss) |
| Largo | New World Symphoney No 9 (Dvorak) |

## Evaluation of the Equipment Selection

All the equipment was selected following our observations on other Snoezelen rooms in neighbouring clinical areas. We soon found that many of our assumptions were not always suitable for this patient group or items we thought were unsuitable proved to be very successful. Following our evaluation of the equipment, we were able to select the most appropriate pieces of equipment and consequently we developed a very specialised Snoezelen room.

\* The Projector and Effect Wheels - Despite their reminiscent properties, we found that the abstract projection wheels were more popular. This was possibly due to the brighter colours which caught the participants attention. By using the familiar projection wheels such as Aviation or The Deep, the participant became focused on the images which monopolised their attention and conversation.

\* Spot Light and Mirror Ball - This piece of equipment was like by most of the participants, however, there were some reports of dizziness and nausea as a result of the constant movement of the light dots. Any reports of these symptoms were resolved by switching off the spot light.

* The Bubble Machine - Although the profusion of bubbles was very successful in encouraging directed movement, the bubble solution made the floor covering very slippery and stained the paint work. The bubble machine was also very noisy and drowned out any background music. As the activity itself was so successful, we returned to using hand held bubble pots and blowing our own.

* The Optic Fibre Spray - Many participants remarked on the beauty of this piece of equipment but few interacted with it. Those who attempted to interact with it, found it soothing and hypnotic.

* The Bubble Unit - The effect of three bubble units was very successful but the mirrors themselves were very distracting. Several participants mistakenly identified their reflection in the mirror as strangers. For some, it created fear as they were unable to communicate with them, for others it encouraged cross remarks such as, "those lazy people over there sitting doing nothing". However, with careful positioning within the room, those most likely to be distracted by the reflections were able to observe the bubble unit without the strangers.

* Aroma Diffuser - This piece of equipment proved to be very popular with the staff using the Snoezelen room and consequently many wards purchased their own diffusers. The aromas chosen were extremely successful so we have continued to explore further into other fragrances.

* Music - The music chosen was essential to complete the atmosphere. Originally, we started with familiar arrangements but we soon found that the 'New Age' music was more suitable. Although the familiar themes were popular, they tended to distract from the other stimuli in the room and monopolised the participant's attention. Therefore, music was chosen for its slow, hypnotic rhythm rather than its melody construction.

## Staff Development

Training the staff was an important part of the installation of Snoezelen. People using the Snoezelen with the elderly confused were to be trained and untrained staff and carers. Initially, Snoezelen study data were set up to allow people to experience the environment for themselves and ask any questions about the concept. These were well attended and demonstrated commitment to the project. We felt the 'new age' feel to the room would deter older carers off the idea but they were some of the enthusiastic attenders. Allowing time for exploration of the room helped staff and carers to try out different approaches and identify different needs. They were able to experiment with lengths of time spent in the room as well as interacting with different pieces of equipment. More formal training sessions allowed for discussion on the theory behind the Snoezelen concept with time for questions on the operating procedures and operational policy.

## THE APPROACH DEVELOPED FOR SNOEZELEN WITH THE ELDERLY

The approach used for this client group was established following a pilot study prior to research carried out in this area and from observations made by the staff and carers. Although this was a very personal interpretation, we had very little information to start with and constantly reviewed and adapted our approach as we proceeded.

Before introducing the patient to Snoezelen, we exposed them to some of the isolated principles to establish what their reaction might be. For those with a higher level of comprehension, we informed them of the concept of Snoezelen.

### Prior to Snoezelen

Patients attending the room were offered the toilet before hand and reminded of the length of time they would be spending in the Snoezelen room. Each participant was given a Snoezelen time that predictably would have the optimum effect, ie mornings for the more restless patients who wanted to go home and afternoon for those whose level of agitation increased after lunch.

The time of day chosen for the sessions was of paramount importance. The sessions were not to be too near any meal times or visiting time as participants would be preoccupied with these future events. Afternoon sessions were also not as successful as participants were often too drowsy or restless about returning to the ward or home. Concentration and enjoyment were greatly increased if the morning session was used when participants were more alert and willing to try the Snoezelen room.

### The Snoezelen Experience

Introduction to the room also required some careful thought. There was often a reluctance to enter a darkened room with strange light patterns so the session was often started with the main fluorescent light on. Once the participants were in the room, we were then able to switch the main light off and introduce the light features one at a time. Although the participants enjoyed the different features of the room, there were some reports of dizziness and nausea with the spot light and mirror ball.

## Bringing Snoezelen to a Close

Bringing patients out of the Snoezelen environment was as equally important. This was started by gradually switching out the light features and reinstating the main lighting. Participants were moved out of the room at their own pace preferably into a quiet environment. Participants leaving the Snoezelen room appeared far more aware of their environment and responded more appropriately to stimuli around them. Staff and carers commented on how relaxed they felt and of their pleasure of being in the Snoezelen environment.

## Creating the Approach, Attitude and Philosophy

Many of the factors that influenced our use of Snoezelen were based on activity that was already being carried out within the hospital environment. We wished to create an atmosphere that was therapeutic, that was flexible enough to meet the needs of individuals and developed correct fundamental attitudes.

Creating the right atmosphere within the Snoezelen room was relatively easy with the basic components of sensory stimulation but it was still important to create an atmosphere that would be accepted by this generation. We had been particularly concerned to create the right atmosphere on the wards and had endeavoured to do so by the use of reminiscence materials and thoughtful interior decorating. These same principles were needed within the Snoezelen to make it acceptable to the patients who would be using it. As the environment itself was conceivably 'hi-tec', we endeavoured to make it more homely with crochet blankets for cosiness and familiar projections on the walls.

We also wanted to create the right atmosphere for the staff using it and all suggestions given by staff and carers were given careful consideration.

Once in the room, the patients were given the opportunity of choice regarding seating and Snoezelen activity. The concept of failure free activity was of paramount importance and any activity the participant wished to indulge was met with total support. Initially, our fears were for the equipment which appeared fairly fragile but during our past year of 'Snoezeling', we have not had any breakages or damages. Most of the participants preferred to observe rather than interact, whatever their preference, they took the lead.

The role of the member of staff or carer assisting the participant was to facilitate any activity if necessary or present the options available to the participant. For most, it was sharing of the experience. The length of time spent in the room was also dictated by the participant but the optimum time appeared to be half an hour.

As many of the participants had few verbal skills, staff who were most familiar with their methods of communication accompanied them in the Snoezelen so that they were able to respond immediately to the participant's wishes. Initially some of the participants endeavoured to rationalise the experience but we soon found that the atmosphere of the room took over.

Certainly, some participants were more responsive to the room than others so each person set their own pace. The participants desire to end the activity, dictated by their restlessness or vocal indications to the person assisting them, was the signal to wind up the activity. Any activity based on atmosphere required careful completion being a very emotive experience. The length of time taken to complete this again was controlled by the participant and their reactions. Identifying these signals was the responsibility of the member of staff or the carer. Creating the right attitude was a concept that needed to be developed prior to the installation of the Snoezelen. Working with the elderly mentally confused is very much concerned with us taking control as part of the caring philosophy. Snoezelen took away this control and allowed the participant to take back some independence of their own.

We needed to be aware of our own attitudes and feelings before we were able to utilise Snoezelen to its full. Time was spent allowing staff and carers to experience the room and explore their own feelings and reactions to the environment before trying to take a patient in. (Anyone who disliked the experience was not expected to take a patient in as this could transfer across to her members in the room). The experience aimed to be shared by all, each gaining and sharing from each others reactions and feelings.

Personal reactions and feelings influenced the way we approached and interacted with the patients we worked with, therefore staff and carers had to be sure about their commitment to the approach. Previous research had shown us that activities such as Reminiscence Therapy, which is beneficial to the patient, was of little personal satisfaction to the group leader. We were concerned that Snoezelen should not suffer the same fate. Fortunately, as Snoezelen proved to be failure free, staff and carers gained certain levels of satisfaction having been part of a successful group.

## RESEARCH BACKGROUND

Before embarking on this project, we made an exhaustive literature search of available material surrounding Snoezelen and the elderly confused. Very little had been written and we were left with more questions than answers. Through support from other clinical areas using Snoezelen, we were able to establish several hypothesis which would be tested to explore the suitability of Snoezelen with the elderly confused. These were based on reducing levels of agitation and negative behaviours.

Previous research had concentrated on Snoezelen as a leisure resource but we felt that for some of our patients, this could be a very therapeutic experience. The research would endeavour to quantify some of the behaviours exhibited by participants while in the Snoezelen room compared with behaviours exhibited during daily activity. This would be compared on a multi-baseline to allow for the deterioration in their mental state which is an inevitable part of Dementia. We also wished to high-light the observations and feelings of the carers who were managing the patient at home. Staff were asked for their opinions of Snoezelen to ensure we would be embarking on a concept which would have their support.

This research project took eighteen months to complete and involved a multi-disciplinary team comprising Occupational Therapy Psychology and Nursing staff. From this, we were able to identify our way forward and take Snoezelen one step forward.

## THE WAY FORWARD

We have had our Snoezelen room for just over a year now and have been able to develop a concept that is unique to our patient group in that short time.

The way forward for us lies in taking Snoezelen into the community, not the fully developed room in its entirety with light and special effects but the philosophy and attitude. For us Snoezelen has developed not as a concrete 'therapy' but a practice that can benefit all who indulge in it. Our Snoezelen concept has moved out of the room into the wards. Staff are selecting periods during the day when emotive music can be played, the aroma diffuser is refilled with carefully selected oils and the lighting is dimmed. Staff, carers and patients can start to relax and take in the atmosphere. Even outsiders are beginning to comment on the 'peacefulness' of these sessions.

### Snoezelen at Home

Carers are being encouraged to consider elements of Snoezelen to use at home following experience in our Snoezelen room. Time has been set aside for carers to explore Snoezelen and ask any questions. This is a concept which encourages a very new experience. The medical model dictates that treatment involves only treating the damaged part, not the whole person and certainly not their carer as well!

Since opening, we have had many enquiries from other hospitals, Nursing Homes and Rest Homes caring for the elderly confused. Snoezelen for the elderly is an emerging concept unique to itself.


## CONCLUSION

Despite the infancy of the concept, Snoezelen with the elderly confused has made great progress in developing its own approach, style and therapeutic outcome.

Its growth has high-lighted five major points which, although may be shared with other clinical areas, are particularly significant for the elderly population.

The approach has particular value in the development of a 'therapeutic relationship'. Although the emphasis is not on therapy, this concept is possible one of the most therapeutic experiences that these patients may have had. Although staff spend time with individual patients, Snoezelen provides them with 'quality' time. It is also an experience that most are keen to repeat.

Time in the Snoezelen environment allows for development of trust, sharing and equality. Everyone can participate in Snoezelen and enjoy the feelings it provokes. By developing a close relationship between ourselves and our patients, we are more likely to succeed with other conventional therapies. By encouraging the equality of the relationship, carers are more comfortable in taking part. This is something that they can share on a partnership basis, for a short while the responsibility is shared. Their role of carer is temporarily dropped for the role of husband, wife, son or daughter - fellow human being.

The activity of Snoezeling is totally failure free and non-directive. For members of staff, this is more rewarding, for carers this is something that can be achieved and for the patients themselves, this avoids the feelings of uselessness. Few other activities can claim these facts.

The principles can be used on the wards or at home. This is an approach that can be adapted to different environments.

Many people have the basic elements of a Snoezelen at home and with careful thought a room or a corner could be set aside for this purpose. Lighting can be adapted with tinted light bulbs, favourite pieces of sensory stimulating music could be played, a small aroma burner or joss stick used and the visual effects could be achieved simply watching the flames of a coal fire or watching fish in a fish tank.

Cognitive ability in the elderly confused is difficult to measure scientifically. However, the principles of Snoezelen appear to stimulate and maintain the body's ability to receive information through all the sensory modalities.

H Bower MD '67 described a 'disuse atrophy' that occurred in elderly confused patients. He stated that the fewer the demands on the sensory modalities, the fewer the neurological responses. This reinforces the need for Snoezelen to move out of the individual treatment session and into the daily life of all our patients. Although the effects of Snoezelen in this form have not been research, they are being seen to be having a positive effect and must be the way forward.

## ACKNOWLEDGEMENTS

Thank you to all the staff, patients and carers who have supported this development during the last eighteen months.

### REFERENCES

Green J G. Measuring Behavioural Disturbances of Elderly Demented Patients in the Community and its Effects on Relatives: A Factor Analytic Study. Age and Ageing Vol 11: 121-126 (1982).

Green J G. Reality Orientation with Elderly Patients in the Community: An Empirical Evaluation. Age and Ageing, Vol 12: 38-43 (1983).

Hagger I, Hutchinson R. Snoezelen: An Approach to the Provision of a Leisure Resource for People with Profound and Multiple Handicaps. Mental Handicap. Vol 19: 51-55 (1991).

Hulsegge J, Verheul A. Snoezelen: Another World, Rompa (1987).

Kewin J, Hutchinson R, Hagger L. The Whittington Hall Snoezelen Project. North Derbyshire Health Authority (1991).

Long A P, Haig L. How do Clients Benefit from Snoezelen? An Exploratory Study. British Journal Occupational Theraphy. Vol 55: 103-106 (1992).

Hutchinson R. Sensory Environment: Ideas about Design and Application. North Derbyshire Health Authority (1992).

King L J. A Sensory Integrative Approach to Schizophrenia. American Journal Occupational Theraphy Vol 28: 529-536 (1974).

Glover E, Mesibov G. An Interest Centre Sensory Stimulation Programme for Severely and Profoundly Retarded Children. Education and Training of the Mentally Retarded. Vol 13: 172-176 (1978).

Bower, M M H. Sensory Stimulation and the Treatment of Senile Dementia. The Medical Journal of Australia Vol 1: 1113-1119 (1967).

Norberg A, Merlin E. Reactions to Music, Touch and Object Presentation in the Final Stages of Dementia. An Explorative Study. International Journal of Nursing Studies Vol 23: 315-323 (1986).

Ayres A J. Sensory Integration and Learning Disorders. California. Western Psychological Services (1983).

# SNOEZELEN - Experiences from a day hospital for adults with mental difficulties

**Kate Smith**
**Pauline McAllister**

## INTRODUCTION

May 1991 saw the introduction of Snoezelen to the Psychiatric Day Unit at Chesterfield Royal Hospital.

Snoezelen was originally developed in Holland over 10 years ago and is now well known internationally. The concept of Snoezelen was originally designed to stimulate the senses of people who have profound learning difficulties and is now looked on as an accepted form of intervention.

The main rationale for developing Snoezelen at Whittington Hall Hospital, Chesterfield was a recognition that two of the basic needs people have are, rest and relaxation. Cunningham et al (1989) defined recreational activities as being not merely resting but the feeling of restoration and refreshment which one attains from engaging in stimulating activities which are free from pressure and enjoyed for their own sake. Snoezelen has been evaluated to two years at Whittington Hall Hospital and their findings have shown that there are major benefits to users. The main benefit was that it had a gentle, stimulating and soothing effect that helped to relieve agitation. It became clear to use that apart from sensory stimulation and enjoyment from the activity, one of the 'side effects' was that patients with profound learning difficulties became less aggressive and more settled after being 'Snoezeled'. To us, it was a clear indication that the calming elements could be utilised for people with mental health problems.

Initially, we evaluated the Snoezelen equipment over a period of three months. We wanted to investigate the possibility of using Snoezelen as an alternative to the traditional methods of relaxation.

## THE WHITE ROOM

The Snoezelen facility can comprise of many areas, which provide a comprehensive library of stimulation. The one that was adapted for use at the Psychiatric Day Unit (PDU) was the White Room. This is a room as the name suggests, white in colour, designed for deep relaxation. Most of our clients suffer from depression and anxiety related illnesses and therefore the White Room facility was found to be the most appropriate.

The equipment comprises of lights, soft music and comfortable chairs that create an atmosphere of calm, enjoyment and security.

Equipment included:

| | |
|---|---|
| Lighting | Projector with effect wheels |
| | Spot lamps with changing colours |
| | Rotating mirror ball |
| | |
| Focal Point | Square light box |
| Bubble Tube | Fibre optic strands |
| | |
| Sounds | Tape player - preferably with constant play facility |
| | Selection of soft music |
| | |
| Walls | Pale coloured, to reflect pastel shades |
| | |
| Smells | Armotherapy unit in which appropriate essential oils are used |
| | |
| Touch | Vibrating bendy tube |

The room was situated in the Day Unit, the clients using the room came from both the day unit and three acute wards. Our room was small in size. It measured approximately 2.27m x 4.00m. We have a reclining chair and a seating unit smothered in pillows offering a choice of sitting or lying positions. Originally, we draped the room in sheets give in a tended effect to the ceiling. It gave the room a soft billowy effect but we had to discard these because it infringed health and safety regulations. We have personalised the room by adding floaty scarves, mobiles and by the use of favourite perfumes as well as the oils. The music we used was also a matter of personal taste, one young girl brought in her own heavy metal rock tapes!

In setting up the White Room, we followed the guidelines suggested by the Whittington Hall Snoezelen Project, IE.

The room was in a quiet area of the unit so that interruptions were unlikely, away from through traffic. The natural light was excluded, the atmosphere we created felt safe and inviting. Harsh lighting and hard surfaces were avoided. Lighting equipment could be used individually or combined to create different effects. Too many lights could create a confusing atmosphere.

## SELECTION CRITERIA

Before using the White Room, clients suitability was assessed. However, as this was a new experience to both staff and clients, part of their suitability wasn't realised until they were in the room. It was important therefore for a member of staff to be present on each initial visit. We found it was best to deter people from using the room who were experiencing an acute psychotic episode as it may have over stimulated them, thus accentuating their symptoms.

We were keen as staff at the unit to make the White Room a success following the outstanding success of the Whittington Hall Project. We know this outcome largely depended on our own attitudes and enthusiasms. Because this concept was very new it has to be our enthusiasm that persuaded clients to try out this new facility. Initial reactions to the room varied from a reluctance to enter an unknown environment to an eager anticipation of what lay ahead. We observed that after the initial reaction to the room, peoples facial expressions relaxed and body postures became more open. They either focused on a particular piece of equipment or became absorbed by the whole environment.

We evaluated the benefits of the White Room for the first three months of use to give us an indication of its usefulness.

Clients both from the day unit and the wards were given a questionnaire on their second visit to the room.

From the questionnaire, all the comments were positive. It was found to be an enjoyable experience by all who used it. All the equipment was liked, although less popular was the bendy vibrating tube. People found it soothing and relaxing and felt they could use the room as time away from stressful situations. Some who found difficulty in sleeping found they could fall asleep more easily. Our hypothesis about the White Room being used as an alternative form of relaxation at that time was confirmed.

We look in more detail at traditional methods of relaxation and compared them with the Snoezelen White Room.

## Differences Between Traditional Relaxation Techniques and Snoezelen Relaxation Room

| RELAXATION | SNOEZELEN |
|---|---|
| **Benefits** | **Perceived Benefits** |
| Dispels fatigue | Pressure taken away from those |
| Decreases pain and | who encounter difficulties increases |
| toleration | with other techniques |
| to pain | |
| Creates feeling of well- | |
| being | |
| Aids sleep | Mind allowed to slow down and |
| Counteracts effects of | wander |
| high levels of arousal | |
| and stress | |
| **Principles** | **Principles** |
| Skill learning techniques | Gentle stimulation leading to |
| Regular practice | relaxation |
| Knowledge of tension and | Emphasis on leisure and |
| relaxation needed | pleasure = therapy leading to |
| Improve coping ability | decrease of symptoms of |
| and change reaction to | tension and anxiety |
| problems | Time away, distraction from |
| Personal responsibility | stressful situations |
| needed | |
| **Techniques used** | **Techniques used** |
| Awareness of posture | No techniques |
| Correct breathing | The relaxing environment is |
| 1 Emphasis on rhythm not | experienced and enjoyed |
| pace | |
| 2 Use of diaphragm | Choice of the individual |
| 3 Focus on out breath | Focus on and absorption in |
| Full concentration needed | certain pieces of equipment |
| Contrast between tension | encourages relaxation |

and relaxation                    Concentration not important
Visualisation:
 Body getting heavier
 Pleasant scene/image
Self talk:
 Suggesting muscles let
 go of tension.

## Benefits of White Room

1    Snoezelen - As an introduction to relaxation group.
     Helps to alleviate anxiety about joining group.

2    Acute illness - eg depression, slowed thought processes impair the
     clients ability to concentrate. Need to make the client feel safe,
     establish rapport.

3    Hearing difficulties, may disturb other members of group, useful
     with deaf clients.

4    Concentrates on the here and now, a transitory sensory experience,
     a short time needed to encourage relaxation. Good for acutely
     agitated.

5    Pressure and intensity reduced in learning techniques, relaxation
     happens.

## Benefits of Traditional

1    Transfer of skills to more realistic situations

2    Coping skills developed, can counter stress themselves

3    No special equipment needed, anywhere, anytime.

## COUNSELLING

We have discovered that for some clients, the White Room has served to enhance the
counselling relationship. The ideal counselling relationship begins in creating a safe and
trusting environment. It is about offering caring and warmth and acceptance of the

client, giving the client unconditional positive regard.

We need to use our skills to the best advantage and for people who find formal counselling sessions difficult, the White Room offers a more relaxed way of establishing a rapport. It can give the relationship a 'kick start'.

The equipment offers distraction and eliminates pressure to talk. It adds almost a social element to the situation and somehow creates openings in conversation. The informal environment facilitate a more relaxed form of communication with the focus still on their particular problem.

We found that initially, anxiety and defensiveness limited self-disclosure by using the White Room, the feelings of safety and security that the room seemed to create, encouraged openness and honesty on the part of the client. This has been demonstrated on several occasions.

One case was a young mother who was suffering from depression and anxiety. She was experiencing problems with her marriage. Formal counselling sessions were difficult, and proved unfruitful. The White Room was tried and within a short period of time this lady had disclosed sexual abuse which had occurred in her teenage years. She had been abused by two different people and one of whom she dare not tell anyone about in case she had not been believed. This proved to be a breakthrough for her and although further sessions were needed, the initial disclosure we feel was due to the security of the room offered.

## CRISIS INTERVENTION

The White Room is fast becoming a treatment choice for clients who present as being anxious and distressed. At this time, we need to be able to offer prompt response to clients who find themselves in a crisis situation, in order to help them gain their emotional equilibrium.

When an individual equilibrium is threatened, stress is increased and feelings of tension occur. At this point, individuals will be able to utilise problem solving skills when stress increases to such a level where tension is heightened and there is overwhelming discomfort. At this stage, there is an inability to utilise any problem solving skills effectively due to disorganisation of thoughts and feelings.

This is where the White Room serves to reverse the process. A calming environment at this stage of crisis is required. In the White Room, the client begins to relax and communication is thereby improved. The tension is decreased and the client begins to feel more comfortable and thoughts become less disorganised. The client is then able to look at the problem in a more realistic way and explore possible solutions. We don't make claims to the White Room being the only solution to an individuals problems but it does serve to provide a calming environment and the opportunity for the client to regain control over their symptoms.

## PRACTICAL RUNNING

The practical running of the White Room has become more efficient as time has moved on. We now operate an appointment system which is supervised by one member of staff at the unit. Clients who use the room solely for relaxation purposes are escorted to the room by the delegated member of staff who then encourages them to settle down in the room and helps to create the desired effect.

The client decides on the length of the session but usually 20 to 30 minutes is adequate. Frequency of use of the White Room is dependent on individual choice and availability of the room and in conjunction with their overall treatment programme. Interruption of the sessions have been avoided by having a delegated member of staff responsible for appointments as well as the presence of a large 'Do Not Disturb' sign. Relaxation in the White Room can also take place in small groups. Numbers have to be limited to 3 to 4 people because of the size of the room and the need to maintain intimacy.

## SAFETY

Safety factors to be considered was the use of fire retardant materials in curtaining and furnishings. As mentioned earlier, the drapes we created initially were removed because of potential fire hazard. All the electrical equipment had to be checked by our works department and extra electric sockets were installed to prevent trailing leads and overloading of power points.

The designated member of staff needs to be responsible as far as possible in ensuring that each of the separate items of equipment is turned off after use.

The equipment is designed for continuous use, so maintenance does not present a problem. Bulbs in projectors are changed regularly. Smoking is forbidden at all times.

By the very nature of working with the acutely mentally ill, suicide risk is always a factor to consider. People who are thought to have suicidal ideation or who are felt to be a suicidal risk are not left alone in the room, they are accompanied by a member of staff.

## HOW IT HAS MOVED ON

The White Room has been in use in the unit for over a year now and we still continue to assess its usefulness. We feel we are still developing its uses and expanding its functions and have given it our own stamp of individuality. We have our own reflexologist, who is a member of the nursing staff. She uses the room weekly for individual sessions and finds the room an ideal venue for her practice.

Massage is performed in the room. It is practised by both primary workers and trainee beauticians from the local technical college. The beauticians use it mainly to relieve tensions. Primary workers, in addition to this, use it as a trust building exercise with some clients.

The Room has been used by a self-awareness group as a winding down exercise at the end of a group session. The group had already developed a sense of identity and co-hesiveness and the atmosphere of the Room developed this further because of the intimacy that was created.

New effects for the light projector have been created by individuals within our art group. This participation has been purposeful for these clients who felt a great sense of achievement from this. It has given the individuals the opportunity to put their stamp on the room as well.

We find, because of the high turnover of patients on the wards, the White Room needs to be continually promoted. Its location away from the wards and patients mean they are often unaware of its presence. The ward occupation therapists plays a useful role in this promotion. This often is done during initial assessment for treatment programmes. If it is indicated, the occupational therapists actively encourages the client to 'try it out' and usually spends the first session in the room with them. Alternatively, ward staff are encouraged to spend time with clients in the room.

The occupational therapist further promotes the facility by informing new staff and students about it and keeps other staff up-to-date about clients who have benefited from the White Room. Ward staff play a valuable role in continuing a clients treatment programme by making the White Room available to them outside the day units opening hours. This has proved useful in providing a more continuous service.

The nature of an acute ward, at times, can be unpredictable and behaviour of certain clients can distress others. The White Room can be used as time away from this environment and serves to relieve any stress that could have been created from the ward situation. It can therefore be a spontaneous intervention as well as being part of a structured programme.

The name Snoezelen is unfamiliar to many of our clients and it didn't describe adequately what the Room was about. For this reason, we felt it necessary to change the name to Relaxation Room which is self-explanatory about its purpose and aim.

## PLANS FOR THE FUTURE

We hope to house our Relaxation Room in a permanent location. The Room used at the moment is a converted interview room. The new room will have textured walls, no windows but will be of a similar size. Extra electricity sockets will be installed to eliminate the need for any trailing flexes. We would look more closely at the flooring materials and furniture, aiming to create different seating arrangements to help further choice in aiding relaxation.

One of the drawbacks of the electrical equipment is the extra sound it creates within the room. In particular, the bubble tube emits a continuous humming sound which some clients find irritating. This could be eliminated by housing it behind a perspex screen, making a permanent fixture.

One of the three acute wards is planning to house a selective range of equipment on the ward in one of their single rooms. This will be primarily for individuals suffering from mania and other disturbed conditions and will hopefully alleviate some of the distress and reduce activity levels.

Plans for the Snoezelen can be as diverse and adventurous as imagination permits. Snoezelen in adult mental health has many possibilities, if finance was limitless. One enthusiastic suggestion was to include a jacuzzi!

## SUMMARY

Snoezelen concept is an exciting development in our unit. It has been difficult to evaluate objectively. Due to Snoezelen having very little theoretical background, any analysis has been purely subjectively especially in the field of adult mental health.

Our initial aims have changed. We thought it would be used as an alternative to traditional methods of relaxation. We have found that the main emphasis of traditional methods offer skill learning that can be transferred into everyday situations, whereas Snoezelen activities dealt with the here and now. There is a place for Snoezelen in relationship building. It helps break down the barriers and gives some clients a boost in the initial stages of the relationship. It has the function of introducing people gently to relaxation sessions especially those people who feel uncomfortable in large groups and for those whose impaired ability to concentrate make it difficult to focus on new information.

The use of the room by individual clients, needs to be reviewed regularly in context with their overall treatment package. It is essential that clients do not view it as a way of avoiding social interaction or other therapeutic interventions.

In Learning Disabilities, the emphasis of Snoezelen is that their members participate in enjoyable activities purely for their own sake rather than for therapeutic purposes. However, in adult mental health it is felt to be the therapy and thereby a means to an end. We hope to enable the clients to gain control over their situation and symptoms by offering pressure free time to help them restore more helpful coping strategies.

Snoezelen is an asset to our unit. It fits in well with the character of the place. We have been able to develop and explore new possibilities, offering a wider range of stimulating therapeutic activities. This has added to our repertoire and ability to offer clients a more comprehensive package of care.

**REFERENCES**

Mitchell Laura, Simple Relaxation. Pitman Press (1977)

Snoezelen. The Whittington Hall Snoezelen Project.
North Derbyshire Health Authority (1991).

Benner M P. Mental Health and Psychiatric Nursing.
Springhouse Publishing Company (1988).

Altulsegge and Verheul. Snoezelen - Another World. Rompa (1987)
Jones, R N. The Theory and Practice of Counselling Psychology. Holt,
Reinhard and Winston Ltd. (1982)

Ironbar and Hooper. Self Instruction in Mental Health Nursing. Bailliere Tindall (1983)

Haggar, Hutchinson. Snoezelen - An Approach to the Provision of a Leisure Resource for People with a Profound and Multiple Handicap. Mental Handicap, Vol 19, June 1991.

Brown and Scott and Pullen. Emergency Psychiatry - Churchill Livingstone (1990)

# SNOEZELEN QUESTIONNAIRE

Name .....................................................................................................................

*What type of relaxation did you use before?  Please tick*

1    Tense and Relax

2    Breathing Control

3    Visualisation (Guided Fantasy)

4    Listening to Music

5    Combination

6    Other

7    *What did you think of the Equipment*        Like              Dislike
        Bendy Tube
        Mirror Ball
        Fibre Optic Strand
        Aromatherapy (Smell)
        Wall Images
        Square Light Box
        Bubble Tube

8    *What piece did you like most?*

9    *What about the room  ie:*        Like              Dislike
        The way it is decorated
        The way it is laid out

        Is it comfortable?                              Yes/No

10   *Did you like the music*                         Yes/No

11    *Did you like a staff member present*
      *or would you prefer to be on your*
      *own?*

12    *Was any other activity used?*
      eg: massage

      *If so, was it effective in any way?*

13    *Would you like to use the room again?*

As we are evaluating the Snoezelen room, its benefits both for staff and patients, we would appreciate your comments and any improvements you would like to see. Thank You.

**COMMENTS**

# SENSORY ENVIRONMENTS AND EXPERIENCES
## - Some ideas for their application

Roger Hutchinson

## INTRODUCTION

Sensory environments have been used for a number of years in the field of profound and severe learning disability. These environments have developed in Snoezelen centres in Holland, Belgium and Great Britain. A Snoezelen centre provides pleasurable sensory experience generated in an atmosphere of trust and relaxation. The experiences provided stimulate the primary senses without the need for intellectual activity (1). We recognise that people who have a severe disability frequently find their immediate environment confusing, restricted and unstimulating. This lack of stimulation coupled with dependency upon others for involvement in daily activity can produce a great deal of stress. It is well documented that underactivity as well as overactivity can lead to stress (2). Much of the activity available to people with a severe disability is dependent upon the persons' ability to interpret the sensory stimulation available (eg one of the most common recreational activities for people with a learning disability is watching the television (3) ). Frequently the degree of intellectual activity required renders the stimulation meaningless. It is therefore essential that stimulation of the primary senses is provided using the medium of sight, sound, touch, taste, smell and movement. This stimulation preferably requiring very little interpretation.

Sensory stimulation from an external source can facilitate the generation of an emotional state, from a sense of well-being and elation to one of fear and isolation. We all use external sensory experience to enhance or change our emotional states. If we are tense, we may well have a bath to relax; a particular restaurant may be a favourite as a result of it's atmosphere; a walk in the country may help us to calm ourselves; we change the lighting to reflect or promote a particular mood. Too much or too little noise or light will lead to stress related disorders (4), eg continuous heat over 35 degrees Celsius will lessen work efficiency; poor illumination or glare can cause physical discomfort; attending to several activities at once can lead to a sense of loss or control.

As individuals, we will often cocoon ourselves in sensation to achieve a desired emotional state, eg lying on a warm beach in the sun with the breeze gently cooling our body and waves gently lapping on the shore; removing ourselves from the world by stimulating our auditory senses using a Walkman. We may often specifically set out to abstract ourselves from reality during which detached experiences may occur that have considerable affective components. A day dream can arouse anger, anxiety, joy or an erotic response. Absorption in a book or film will allow the central awareness of the individual to be turned elsewhere. We become absorbed in the sensation (5). It is quite common to feel unhappy and enhance the sensation by playing a particular song or to lessen the extent of a particular emotion using displacement behaviour. A feeling of aggression can be displaced through physical activity.

Essentially, we are able to use sensory stimulation to facilitate the development of desired emotional states.

Sensory stimulation can be used to enhance experience. It is possible to use sensory stimulation in the area of teaching and therapy to make demands upon the individual and promote change. It is equally possible to use sensory stimulation as a major part of leisure activity to provide enjoyment and pleasure. Control by the individual over the sensory stimulation available can increase opportunities for choice. Where sensory stimulation is a major component of a leisure activity and is selected by the individual, the activity is undertaken for its own sake and its major function is recuperation. Sensory stimulation is used to facilitate rest and the overcoming of fatigue. It has a direct effect on lessening the impact of stressors in the individual's life. Regular relaxation can be used to improve the rate of recovery from major surgery or aid in the control of chronic pain. It is now known that stress is a significant component in a variety of physical conditions (6). Currently the use of sensory environments is being explored in maternity services (7); in chronic pain (8); in paediatrics (9); with young people with a physical disability (10); in mental health services (11); with people who are elderly (12) and with people who have profound multiple disabilities (13, 14).

## Relationships

For some individuals, the environment is sufficient to facilitate the desired experience, but for many the desired experience is only possible if that experience is shared with another person. We term the other person in learning disability services as an 'enabler'. This is a person who is involved with the client in a sensitive, caring and non directive way, helping to create an atmosphere of safety and security within which the client can exercise free choice. In a leisure setting, the enabler does not focus on therapeutic outcome, but rather on sharing a common positive emotional experience with the clients. At the other end of the spectrum in an environment focusing upon therapeutic outcome, a therapist will of necessity, intervene in the client's activities, directing the client towards specific experiences which will facilitate the desired outcome. Gentle teaching (15) would appear to fit between these two extremes as its essence is the development of a relationship with the client which is then used to achieve desired therapeutic outcomes. It involves the teaching of bonding to those who have not yet bonded with their care givers.

**SENSORY ENVIRONMENT**

Generally they provide:

1      Thoughtfully designed facilities

2      Stimulation of the primary senses

3      Choice and opportunity for stimulation and relaxation

4      The development of relationships and carers/therapy/support staff

Relationships in these environments help to:

1      Promote communications and sharing

2      Reduce stress

3      Build feelings of worth

The facilities themselves need to:

i)      be accessible to user group

ii)      be valued by therapist and user

iii)      be uncomplicated whenever possible

iv)      offer wide ranging choice

v)      be easily maintained

vi)      be flexible

## STAFF

When using sensory environments staff need:

    i)       to be creative in their use of facilities

    ii)      to be well training

    iii)     value the clients

The education that staff receive must ensure that staff embrace the concepts involved in using sensory environments. When working with people who have a disability, it is essential that staff education enhances the staff communication skills. This will often mean valuing and utilising staff's personal strengths and making decisions about whether the person rather than the professional is more important in certain circumstances. This particularly so when the staff/client relationship is of paramount important in the use of the environment.

## COMMUNICATION

In many instances communication with clients may be difficult as a result of disability of distress, whether as a result of the emotional or physical situation the client finds them self in. Accordingly it is essential that communication:

    i)     is related to the individual needs/abilities of the client

    ii)    is holistic - not just verbal

    iii)   is interactive (staff client communication is often one way!)

    iv)   is responsive to the clients needs at the time

    v)    at times relies more on non verbal means rather than verbal, particularly in the areas of vision and touch (a cuddle can mean more than any amount of supportive counselling).

Sensory environments lead to sensation. Trying to describe a sensation verbally can be the most effective way of stopping it.

Rapport, a concept taken from the Neurolinguistic Programming (Leslie Cameron-

Bandler) can be achieved if the carer matches the "predicates" of the person with a disability they are interacting with. People organise their world with respect to sight, sound, touch, smell, movement. These sensory experiences are organised into a prepresentational system and it is possible to tell which representational system a person is using. People with verbal language use classes of words many of which reflect specific sensory modalities, these classes of words are termed "predicates". By understanding the representational system that the person uses, and using that system when interacting with the person, the person will feel understood as at the unconscious level the person will have the experience of being understood. In addition he/she will more easily understand the carers since the carer will be literally speaking his/her language. This is the basis for rapport.

For example:

| Statement | Predicate | Representational System |
|---|---|---|
| I can see that now | see | visual |
| I have a feeling for that | feeling | kinaesthetic |
| I'm in the tune with that | tune | auditory |

Predicates allow the carer to know what aspect of sensory experience the clients is most conscious of and is most relevant to him or her at that moment. Where verbal communication is limited or is not possible, representation systems can be identified by careful observation of the person with a disability to identify those sensory experiences to which the person makes a response. Once the primary representational system is known, communication can take place using touch, sound, vision, etc. If the person can use a symbolic language system predicates can be identified.

A further means of communication is to become involved in basic rapport-building patterns by "Matching". This is the process whereby a person adjusts the same aspects of their external behaviour to approximate those same aspects of the other persons external behaviour. The on-going process of matching is known as "Pacing". That is one person moves as the other moves, matching his or her movements. Matching behavioural outputs can lead to the creation of very powerful states of rapport, both consciously and unconsciously. In severe and profound multiple disability, one of the major ways of having a dialogue with the client is to identify rapport-building patterns by becoming involved in matching activity. Matching activity underpins much of the "Enabling" approach as it involves developing an intimate sensitivity to the clients behaviour. Examples of matching activity are set out in Table 1.

## *MATCHING - Table 1*

| | |
|---|---|
| WHOLE BODY MATCHING: | Adjust your body to approximate the others postural shifts. |
| HALF BODY MATCHING: | Match the upper or lower portion of the persons body |
| PART BODY MATCHING: | Pacing any consistent or stylistic use of body movements, eg. eye blinks |
| HEAD/SHOULDER ANGLE: | Matching characteristic poses that the other person offers with his head/shoulders |
| FACIAL EXPRESSIONS: | See the ways in which the other person uses their face, eg. wrinkling nose, raising eyebrows, puckering lips etc. |
| GESTURES: | Matching the other persons gestures in ways that are graceful and respectful |
| VOCAL (analog) QUALITIES: | Match shifts in tonality, tempo, volume, intonation patterns etc. |
| VERBAL PATTERNS: | Hear and use sensory system predicates that match and pace the sequence of representational system predicates used by the other person |
| REPETITIVE PHRASING: | Hear and utilise the repeated phrases or sound of the other person |
| BREATHING: | Adjust your breathing patterns to match the other persons breathing patterns |

## INDIRECT MATCHING (CROSS-OVER MIRRORING)

Using one aspect of your behaviour to match a **DIFFERENT** aspect of the other persons behaviour, eg. adjusting the tempo of your voice to match the other persons rate of breathing; pacing the other persons eye blinks with your finger or head nods.

## PERCEPTION

The doors of perception are the senses, our eyes, nose, ears, mouth and skin, (Aldous Huxley). These are our only points of contact with the world. The sensations we experience result from the way in which we use "perceptual filters" to limit and organise the sensory input we receive. Thus the world we perceive is not the "real" world but a map made up by our neurology. If we have sensory or cognitive impairments, those senses that are triggered by environmental or internal stimuli often become more able to discriminate, leading to a wider range of sensory experience. However, if we have a severe impairment, the range of sensory stimuli that can be accessed may be limited and the range of sensation experienced reduced. When we think about what we see, hear and feel, we re-create those sights, sounds and feelings inwardly. We re-experience information in the sensory form in which we first experience it. We use our senses outwardly to perceive the world, and inwardly to re-present experiences to ourselves.

The visual system can be used externally when we are looking at the outside world, or internally when we are mentally visualising. In the same way, the auditory systems can be divided into hearing external or internal sounds. Our kinaesthetic (feeling) sense can be focused upon external sensations like touch, temperature and moisture. Internal kinaesthetics include remembered sensations, emotions, and inner feelings of balance and bodily awareness, known as the proproceptive sense which provides us with feedback about our own movements. Usually visual, auditory and kinaesthetic sensations provide our primary representation system. In some cases, however, as a result of sensory or cognitive deficit, the sense of taste, smell, or gustatory experience becomes the primary representation system rather than just providing powerful and immediate links to sights, sounds and feelings associated with them. People have a tendency to favour one particular prepresentational system, although they are not mutually exclusive. It is possible to visualise a scene, have the associated feelings and hear the sounds simultaneously. Often the representational system favoured will be dictated by the sensory environment that the person experiences, (eg. using auditory sensations in a darkened room) or by the persons ability to experience and filter the sensory stimuli present (eg a person whom is autistic using smell).

It is essential to identify the preferred representational system for the client with sensory or cognitive impairments. When a person tends to use a preferred system habitually (either as a result of impairment or as a result of the environmental stimulation that is accessible) they are likely to be more discriminating and are able to make finer distinctions in this system than in others. These discriminations and distinctions are frequently not perceived by other individuals using a different primary representation system. An essential of **"ENABLING"** is to identify the representation system that the client is using at the time, the clients primary representation system, and appreciate the extent to which the client can make distinctions and discriminations within the systems used.

Just as the person has a preferred representational system, so they also have a preferred system for remembering. A complete memory would contain all the sights, sounds, feelings, tastes and smells of the original experience, or those sensations that were accessible to the person. To recall the experience, we prefer to do one of these. Think back to a holiday, what comes first? A picture, sound or feeling. The lead system is the internal sense that we use as a handle to reach back to memory. People often have different lead systems for different types of experiences. Pictures may be used for a painful experience but sounds may generate pleasant ones. Again, it is an essential part of the enabling relationship to identify which is the lead system for which type of experience. For many clients it is also necessary to identify whether there is a difference in the external and internal lead system for a specific type of experience and if so, which is dominant. The child going to the doctors for a painful examination may well recall the experience by "leading" with a kinaesthetic memory of her mothers physical comforting or recall may be triggered by the smell associated with the consulting room. Understanding of the lead system dominant at a given time can help us to understand behaviour which appear to have no obvious environmental trigger. It may be an internal sensory one which has previously been associated with an unpleasant experience. We can also take information from one sense and represent it with another. If my lead system is auditory and my preferred system is visual, I will tend to remember a person by the sound of their voice and think about the person in pictures. Sounds can conjure up visual memories, smells can generate pictures etc. We often have an immediate and unconscious link between our lead and preferred system. This is termed **SYNESTHESIA**. Colours can be linked to moods and sounds can be linked to visual and kinaesthetic sensation.

The 'enabler' should develop an intimacy with the client that allows them to recognise those aspects of behaviour which identify which lead or preferred system the client uses. These behaviours are terms **ACCESSING CUES**. It is very often extremely difficult it identify the preferred and lead systems that the client is using by monitoring their responses in the "ordinary world". When interacting with the client in a sensory environment within which the client can be exposed to discrete and variable sensory stimuli, it is possible to identify which **SUBMODALITIES** of which representation system the client is able to use. Essentially, if representation systems are described as modalities, the submodalities are the building blocks of the senses, combining together to create each sound, picture or feeling. An understanding of the ways in which a person uses submodalities allows identification of access cues used by the client which in turn indicate the representation system used by the client. With this knowledge, it is possible to understand the **PREDICATES** used by the client thereby facilitating the development of **RAPPORT** with the client which in turn leads to the possibility of dialogue with the client. Some common submodality distinctions which can be used when presenting stimuli to ascertain the clients response are:

| **VISUAL** | **AUDITORY** | **KINAESTHETIC** |
|---|---|---|
| Colour/black or white | Stereo or Mono | Location |
| Two or three dimensions | Words or sounds | Intensity |
| Left/right or up/down | Volume (loud/soft) | Pressure (hard/soft |
| Distance from stimuli | Tone (soft/harsh) | Extent (how big) |
| Brightness | Timbre (sound fullness) | Texture |
| Contrast | Location of sound | Weight (light/ heavy) |
| Clarity (blurred or not) | Distance from sound | Temperature |
| Movement | Duration | Duration |
| Speed | Continuous | Shape |
| Number of images | Speed | |
| Size | Clarity (clear or muffled) | |

The ideas outlined in this section and the preceding section considering rapport are taken from Nuro Linguistic Programming reference:

O'Connor J and Seymour J. Introducing Nuro-Linguistic Programming - The New Psychology of Personal Excellence. Mandala, ISBN 1-85274-073-6 (1990).

## DISABILITIES

Sensory environments have a role in all forms of disability. Obviously, the environment would be geared to the type of presenting disability, ie perceptual, sensory, physical, emotional, social, psychological or learning. The environment should be geared to maximising sensation by making the best use of the senses available to the client. The sensory environment can provide a library of stimulation which can break through the perceptual barrier frequently encountered when working with people who have a profound disability, who often have an internal rather than external focus for sensions (16).

Considerations should be given to the Impairment, Disability and Handicap that the individual experiences.

Impairment: The basic Biological/Physiological/Psychological abnormality that is present.

Disability: The Functional Skill Loss resulting from the impairment.

Handicap: The Social Consequences of the disability.

Unless the basic sensory loss that the individual experiences is identified (including any perceptual deficits or disorders of sensory integration, memory etc) it will not be possible to create an environment that is accessible to the individual. Similarly, the design of the environment or sensory experience that is available to the individual should minimise the extent to which the disability the individual presents will actually disable them. The sensory experience available should not further disable the person; eg the person with hearing loss should not be placed in an environment that makes it more difficult to selectively attend to sounds; the person who has just overcome a disability and learnt to walk independently should not be placed in an environment with a softly padded floor. Finally, the experiences provided should not further contribute to the handicap the person experiences as a result of the attitudes of society to their disability. Ideas such as "age appropriateness" should not be used to devalue experiences that the person with a disability enjoys. The question should be asked, "Who is this activity a problem for?

Certainly not the individual involved in, and enjoying the activity. Perhaps the problem lies with the person who does not have the disability and finds difficulty in accepting that people who are "different" should be valued in part because of the differences. Is not this one of the worst forms of prejudice? Providers involved in planning and providing opportunities for sensory experience to people with a disability should plan provision with the same degree of thought, care and resources as are necessary when considering any other minority group in the community with specialised needs. By providing the person with facilities that are evalued by other people in their community who do not have a disability and who can only access these "special" facilities by sharing them with the disabled user, integration does occur in which the majority seeks out the minority to share the minorities resources, rather than the minority having to use facilities designed primarily for the majority of people which have usually been poorly adapted. This strategy could be seen to be "reverse integration".

The environment should be geared to maximising sensations by make the best use of the senses available to the client.

The sensory environment can provide a library of stimulation which can break through the perceptual barrier frequently encountered when working with people who have a profound disability, who often have an internal rather than external focus for sensation (16).

Table 2 outlines a development approach to cognition based upon the sensory experience accessible to the individual. The way we think evolves from the way we feel. This may well be overly simplistic, however, for the person with limited access to sensory experience and a limited capacity to interpret and integrate the experiences they enjoy, of necessity their picture of the world is built upon primary sensory experience. When in distress many people do not function as rational, clear thinking adults who are able to use the process of thought to relieve the stress they are experiencing. Frequently, the only way that staff supporting the individual can enter into a "dialogue" with their patient/client is to initiate (and sometimes maintain) communication through sensory experience. With a sensitive partner a touch, glance, sign or cuddle can mean communicate more than any amount of "supportive counselling". Surely this is also the case when considering supportive care relationships provided by professional staff. These relationships can be enhanced if the "carer" deliberately attempts to provide sensory experiences that the person can enjoy and which are under the persons control. In an intensive care unit in a general hospital, the patient is often disoriented due to their circumstances and medication regime. They are often left to enjoy the stimulation provided by the ward ceiling and as they cannot selectively attend to sensory activity in the surrounding environment are unable to integrate their experiences leading to yet more confusion. There " **LIFE SPACE**" narrows to the point where all their senses are turned inwards focusing upon their pain; or their fears and worries, thereby increasing their level of stress. It is possible to distract the patient by using smell, projected visual patterns, massage, sound. At the very worst, it will be more interesting than the ceiling. If the person is also able to turn particular sensory activities on or off (using a head or movement switch) they can have some control over their immediate experience. Absence of a sense of personal control, or loss of personal control can in some circumstances be a major contributory factor in raising stress levels.

## FROM SENSATION TO COGNITION

| AGE (in months) | <2 months | 2-8 months | <8 months |
|---|---|---|---|
| Neurological substrate maturation | spinal marrow brainstem | limbic system | cerebral cortex |
| awareness | sensation | perception | gnosis and cognition |
| experience | here and now | anticipation | mental |
| memory | 'reflex' or 'body' memory | affective-emotional memory | cognitive memory |
| learning process | classic conditioning excitation-inhibition | operant conditioning trial and error rewarding and punishing | imitation intentionality mental representation symbolic function |
| emotion | comfort-discomfort feelings | differentiation attachement-behaviour | frustration (8 month fear) |
| senses | proprioception nearby senses | distances senses | intersensorial associations |
| attention orientation reflex involuntary attention | arousal reactions | selective attention | continuous attention |
| contact-interaction | body contact muscular dialogue | body language eye contact social smile | language with symbols interaction with a real social dimension |
| locomotion | nureo-motility | senso-motility | psycho-motility |
| motivation | stimulus depended | extrinsic motivation rewarding | intrinsic motivation exploration |

**TABLE 2** *(Taken from reference 16)*

## TOUCH

Touch is often an integral part of activity with clients/patients. In our relationship touch is usually interactive, communicative, pleasurable and sensitive. Professional touch is usually directive, authoritative and insensitive from the client/patient perspective. It does little to promote/enhance positive sensation. For touch to have this function in our professional activities we need to develop policies that provide a framework within which touch can be used and which prevent its abuse.

"Touch is the oldest sense; and the most urgent. Consider all the varieties of pain, irritations, abrasions; all the textures of lick, pat, wipe, fondle, knead; all the prickling, bruising, tingling, brushing, scratching, banging, fumbling, kissing, nudging. Pulling a foot out of mud. The squish of wet sand between the toes. The near orgasmic caravan of pleasure, shiver, pain and the relief that we call a backscratch" (17).

Essentially, vision, hearing, smell, touch, taste and movement can be used to provide sensory experience individually or in combination. They can be available through environmental manipulation or they can be applied to the individual personally. The experiences resulting from sensory stimulation can be used to generate, enhance, reduce or change sensation, contributing to changes in emotional state.

## PRACTICE

Sensory environments can be used with different aims in mind

Experimentally <----------------------->     Task Orientated
Orientated Activity                        Activity

A difference of emphasis may require different operational policies and a different approach by staff

Enabling       <----------------------->     Directed Therapy

It may be necessary to provide a sensory environment that an individual or group can use, or alternatively provide a range of sensation specifically for the individual, allowing the individual to cocoon themselves in sensation, abstracting themselves from the surrounding environment.

Sensory       <----------------------->     Personal (Sensory
Environment                           Cocoon) Sensations

Considerations should be given to the issue of whether the individual can use on environment for a variety of activities as some aims may be incompatible. Can an environment used by an individual for leisure also be used by the same individual for directed intervention by a therapist.

Externally motivated activity

Leisure <-----------------------> Directed Intervention

Internally motivated activity

Environments and activities can be developed which move the focus of the sensory experiences.

| | |
|---|---|
| Externally motivated<br>Directed Intervention | Traditional Assessment and +<br>Therapy. Staff will have a body<br>of knowledge and training.<br>Restrictive practices will operate.<br>Activity will be programmed.<br>Environment will be controlling. |
| Leisure +<br>Internally Motivated | Snoezelen: A creative and<br>flexible environment, unlikely<br>that staff required a specific<br>professional training. |
| Directed Intervention<br>Internally Motivated | Personally enhance leisure +<br>activity to enhance<br>therapeutic benefit.<br>Developmental activity,<br>naturalistic observation.<br>Personally motivated<br>exploration. Staff may<br>require professional training. |

| Externally Motivated leisure + Leisure | Therapist intervenes in activity to enhance therapeutic benefit of leisure. Staff require professional training. |

## SOME IDEAS

Use of a white room to facilitate relaxation. Possible use of relaxation/hypnosis tapes in the white room. The white room can help a group of people to feel more at ease with each other.

A sound and light room can be used for assessment of perception and senses. Can promote motivation if user operable. Jacuzzi/spa pool can promote relaxation, reduction of pain, develop trust, facilitate co-operative activity.

Individual items can provide an experimental environment which will facilitate relaxation, eg a head water bed bathed in pinkish light with a restful or uterine sound played through the bed can rapidly produce a relaxed state. Water, sound and light are used effectively to promote relaxation in childbirth. The lighting in an environment can be altered to provide an atmosphere or intimacy. Environments can be specifically designed to reduce stress or overcome the sensory deprivation resulting from prolonged placement in an unstimulating environment eg intensive care units. The environment can be designed to have an impact via active or passive activity on the part of the user. Aromatherapy/massage changes the individual's sensations.

## THINGS TO COME

Probably the ultimate sensory environment is the environment created by interactive computer technology producing the completely convincing illusion of being immersed in an artificial world that exists only inside a computer. Virtual Reality is the name of this interactive computer technology (18). At the heart of Virtual Reality is an experience - the experience will be able to be tailored to personal wishes or desires or could be produced to promote specific discreet sensory stimulation.

Heilig said in 1962 of his intervention the "Sensorama Simulator";

".... it is an object of the present invention to provide an apparatus to simulate a desired experience by developing sensation in a plurality of the senses .... it is also an object of the invention to provide an apparatus for simulating an actual, predetermined experience in the senses of an individual".

Virtual Reality could be seen to be a high technology version of an environment structured to stimulate the primary senses.

## CONCLUSION

The sensation an individual receives can be structured to promote, change or enhance the individual's sensory experience. This can be achieved through manipulation of the individual's external environment to provide specific or multiple primary sensations or the individual can experience personal primary sensation through active or passive involvement in sensory activity. As sensory experience is directly related to emotional state, sensation can be provided which contributed to the development of emotional states which are of therapeutic value to the individual concerned.

### REFERENCES

1    Kewin J. Snoezelen User Guide in Hutchinson R (ed). The Whittington Hall Snoezelen Project, North Derbyshire Health Authority (1990).

2    Clarke D. Stress Management, Cambridge: National Extension College (1989).

3    Lambe I and Hogg J. People with profound retardation and multiple handicaps attending schools or social education centres. Final Report. Pipler Hill School, Manchester (1987).

4    Hutchinson R. An exploration of the uses of sensory environments as an aid to the reduction of work related stress in proceeding of 10th International Conference on Off share Search and Rescue, Marine Communications, Marine and Aviation Safety. Leith International Conferences, Milton Road East, Edinburgh (1991).

5    Arle HWA and Boys H. Hypnotherapy. A Practical Handbook. Free Association Books, London (1987).

6    Pearce S and Wardley J (eds). The Practice of Behavioural Medicine, British Psychological Society (1989).

7    Maternity Unit. Christina Hartley Hospital, Southport.

8    Chronic Pain Clinic. North Derbyshire Royal Hospital, Chesterfield (Pat Schofield)

9    Children, CDC. Northampton and North Ayre Community Nursery.

10   Physical Disability. St Lukes Hospital, Huddersfield

11   Psychiatric Day Hospital. North Derbyshire Royal Hospital, Chesterfield.

12      Community Hospital. Bolsover (Nr Chesterfield) and King Park Unit. Bournemouth.

13      Whittington Hall Hospital, Chesterfield.

14      Sint Oda, Overpelt, Belgium

15      Jones R. Gentle Teaching in Jones R and Eairs C. Challenging Behaviour and Mental Handicap; a psychological perspective. BIMH, Kidderminster (1990).

16      Cohen L, Salapetek P. From Sensation to Cognition, Academic Press, New York (19975).

17      Ackerman D. A Natural History of the Senses, Random House, New York (1990).

18      Rheingold H. Virtual Reality, Seeker and Warburg, Great Britain (1991).

# THE ROLE OF SENSATION IN THE MANAGEMENT OF CHRONIC PAIN

Pat Scholfield

## INTRODUCTION

### The History of Pain Management

The Pain Management Service in Chesterfield was first established in 1976. Initially, "Pain Clinics" as they were then known attempted to relieve pain using repeated injections of local anaesthetics to "freeze" nerves. In 1965, the Gate Control theory of pain was introduced (Melzach and Wall) using the concept of a gate within the spine which can be opened and closed by various mechanisms, including central control (the brain). This concept is the one most readily accepted by medical practitioners today thus explaining why techniques such as relaxation and distraction can be successful in overriding the pain sensation. During this time, it also became recognised that medical science does not have all of the answers and that pain like the person is composed of many factors, which can influence the way the individual can cope with disease or illness. Therefore, the management of people with pain utilises the multi-disciplinary approach. A team was developed in Chesterfield consisting of Doctors, Psychologists, Nurse Specialists, Physiotherapists and Social Workers who could together deal with the many aspects of the patient in pain. The priority of care moved away from solely physical therapy to multifaceted management.

As the emphasis moves away from purely physical care to psychosocial care, so the potential for providing an environment of pleasant sensory experiences can be recognised. However, before this potential can be explored, there is a need to understand the aspects of pain and its current management.

### What is pain

Pain has been described as "an unpleasant sensory of emotional experience associated with actual or potential tissue damage, or described in terms of such damage" (I.A.S.P. 1986). Throughout history, pain has been discussed within mystical, spiritual and religious structures. Often it has been viewed as a punishment from God, or a way of purging the soul. The world "pain" is derived from the Latin world "Poena" which means punishment. Aristotle viewed pain as a negative passion; a feeling state opposite to pleasure, postulating that the heart was the centre of sensation. Descartes, however, changed western thinking by suggesting the brain as the centre of sensation with pain pathways but with a gate mechanism which can be opened or closed by various mechanisms either blocking or allowing the pain pathway. Research is still being carried out to answer all of the questions related to the physical cause of pain which is only one factor in the complicated puzzle of pain.

## Factors influencing pain perception

If pain was purely a physical stimuli then physical treatments would be the answer. However, it is much more complicated than that. Carers are adopting the Holistic approach to careing, which is looking after the whole person. Therefore, carers must consider all aspects of the patients psychology, sociologicial background and cultural background when dealing with the person in pain.

## Psychological Factors

Personality is a blend of intellectual and emotional qualities reflected in the behaviour of the individual. A knowledge of the patients personality prior to development of the illness will enable carers to predict which the patient will utilise to cope with the stresses and strains of life. Individuals can be divided into groups with common characteristics of emotions known as personality traits (Bond 1979). The are:

1    **Anxiety** - The person who worries about everything.
     Anxiety levels are raised when in pain which heightens
     the level of pain.

2    **Depression** - Often people can have a feeling of low spiritedness
     when faced with traumatic experiences such as bereavement. The
     depressive personality quickly reaches desperation and cannot cope
     which then exacerbates the pain.

3    **Hysterical** - These individuals usually exhibit immaturity in
     emotions and behaviour. When the pain experience occurs, these
     people exaggerate symptoms usually becoming demanding and
     manipulative. "Hysterics" can then occur.

4    **Hypochondriacal** - Individuals who have a tendency to worry
     about health matters and bodily functions, resulting in frequent
     visits to the doctor. Often all that is needed is reassurance.

5    **Obsessional** - Punctuality, reliability, opposition to change,
     meticulousness, are all characteristics of this personality. The

world has to be black and white, grey areas such as pain are not coped with at all.

Various methods are available to assess personality (M.M.P.I. E.P.I) which can be useful in the management of pain.

## Social and Environmental Factors

These factors cannot alter the pain sensation but they can affect how the individual reacts to the pain. How individuals are treated in childhood in relation to pain sets a pattern of behaviour in adults. Also the meaning of the pain to the individual can be influential. If the pain serves no purpose other than to destroy a way of life, it can be exacerbated by the losses which it brings about. This is invariably the case with chronic pain. There has also been much research into the effects of age, gender, education, marital status and compensation (Painter 1980, Guck 1986, Aronoff and Evans 1982). The evidence, however, is conflicting.

## Cultural Factors

Vast cultural differences have been noted (Zborowski 1952, Madjar 1985, Strelzer and Wade 1981) in peoples behaviour and attitudes towards pain. From the "crying and moaning" of the Italians to the "stiff upper lip" of the British. These factors cannot affect the amount of pain felt but they do affect how the patient assessed their pain.

## Stress

Increasingly, it is believed that stress is an inevitable part of life. During the past 40 years, many definitions of stress have been made. Most consider it to be an event which disrupts or disturbs the individual, or a state of disturbance in an individual (Holmes and Rahe 1967, Seyle 1956). Environmental events which are sources of stress are known as "stressors"; these are major life events such as divorce or bereavement. Minor events or ongoing stresses related perhaps to finance or work are known as "Hassles". Research has demonstrated stressful events and daily hassles to be associated with chronic pain. Chronic pain in itself can result in one or more major stressful life events which can be loss of job due to the pain which then leads to hassles or strains over finances (Sternback 1986). People respond to stress in different ways, perhaps with anger, depression, anxiety or denial. This reaction is known as "coping".

## Acute and Chronic Pain

If an individual puts their hands onto a hot stove, the pain which they will experience is described as acute. It is a warning sign that something is wrong and it will prevent the individual from additional damage by causing them to remove their hand quickly. Most people have experienced acute pain at some time during their lives; it could be anything from toothache to major trauma. In time, the pain will subside either with self help or medical intervention, when the disease or injury has healed.

Chronic pain is a daily occurrence of pain described as being of over six months duration. It may develop for no apparent reason and continues despite medical intervention. The longer the pain is present, the more the psychological and social factors influence the course of the syndrome; causing great emotional distress. With social isolation, loss of job, status, family disturbances, financial worries, inactivity which may lead to deformity, anger depression, loss of sleep, frustration and the constant worry that the pain must be due to a serious disease. These are the people who are referred to the pain service, usually after months or years of investigations and treatments by their General Practitioner or other consultants. Hence the multi-disciplinary approach to their problems is required.

Management by medication and injection therapy may be necessary but primarily the aim is to help these people to understand that pain can be prevented without an obvious physical cause and they can can continue to be useful members of society despite a degree of ongoing pain. In order to carry out this re-education, pain management programmes have been developed.

## Chronic Pain in Society

Large scale national epidemologic studies have been carried out on incidence, prevalence, economic impact, deographic characteristics and many other impacts of most diseases and health care problems. Data is available on cancer, heart diseases, diabetes and many others. There is, however, no data available on large scale national survey of incidence, prevalence and social and economic cost of chronic pain. In the 1960's John Bonica attempted to rectify this by making estimates regarding the incidence of chronic pain in America, and subsequent estimates regarding chronic pain in other countries.

Local surveys were reviewed and found to be sufficiently similar. At the First World War Congress on Pain (1975) suggested guidelines were given to carry out these studies. It was recommended that data be collected on the magnitutde of chronic pain syndromes, frequency, causes, impacts on families and society, treatments and their outcomes. The results of this recommended survey should be available in the near future.

The estimates presented by Bonica *(1990) were supported by others (Crook et al 1984, Taylor 1985) and they suggested the following:

> More than one third of the American population has chronic painful conditions resulting in excess of 400 million working days lost. 120 million days are lost due to back pain. An estimated 31 million Americans have back pain.
>
> The implications of these findings are financially and socially phenomenal due to the loss of productivity, cost of benefits, medication and treatment.
>
> The consensus of findings in America would suggest the possibility of similar findings in the UK.

## Pain Management

As far back as 1945, it was realised how complex the problem of chronic pain is, therefore, the multi-disciplinary team approach was introduced. It was during the 1970's that the behavioural approach to pain management was introduced (Fordyce 1976). It was demonstrated that profound changes could be made in the patients behaviour without treating the cause of the pain. This was the inception of pain management programmes which spread all over America and then other parts of the world.

Specific methods of management are used in varying degrees in most countries. Logistically, it is not possible for all programmes to use every method of management. Also, programmes may be inpatient or outpatient depending on facilities. Programmes may use all or some of the following techniques:

 *1  Assessment - medical/psychological
 *2  Diagnostic procedures
 *3  Medical treatment
 *4  Physical therapy
 *5  Occupational therapy
 *6  Psychological treatment
 *7  Vocational counselling
 *8  Family therapy
 *9  Nerve blocks/trigger point injections

*10    Acupuncture
11    Biofeedback
*12    Relaxation training
13    Autogenic training
*14    Education
*15    Assertiveness training
16    Communication training
*17    Massage therapy
*18    T.C.N.S. (Transcutaneous electrical nerve stimulation)
19    Ablative neurosurgery
20    Implanted stimulators

(* indicate techniques used in Chesterfield)

The modalities most relevant to application within a sensory environment are as follows:

Physical therapy, family therapy, relaxation training, education and massage therapy. Applications will be discussed in more detail.

## The Role of Sensation

The smell of freshly brewed coffee, the sound of a particular piece of music, a beautiful view, the test of a favourite food and the feel of satin or velvet; these are experiences of the senses which can bring back pleasurable memories. The newborn baby can recognise its Mother by her smell or the sound of her voice. Gradually during development, the baby learns to sort and name these sensations. Even at such an early age, the senses are so finely tuned. On reaching adulthood, the senses are taken for granted and not appreciated fully. Helen Keller wrote in greater detail about wonderful smells, tastes and textures. Although she possessed only three of the five senses, it was said that she was "more alive than many people of her generation".

Nothing is more memorable than a smell, it can conjure memories as far back as childhood. Encountering the smell again can set a person daydreaming, reliving the experience. Women in their quest to be attractive have throughout history applied perfume. Incense was mentioned as far back as the Bible.

Using touch can make the world three dimensional. Losing touch can make people feel strange (local anaesthetic given at the dentist). The newborn baby feels comfort in its mothers arms and this feeling of comfort when being held close continues throughout life. Touch can be reassuring, it can break down carer/patient barriers. For example, holding the hand of a dying patient, letting them know they are not alone. Touch can also be therapeutic (Krieger 1979). If an individual bumps their leg, they help take the pain away by rubbing the area, this massage can be very soothing. It is believed that massage increases blood flow, relaxes muscle spasm and the technique can help patients feel generally relaxed. Scientifically, it is believed that massage can close the pain gate and encourage the release of the endorphins within the body (these are the natural pain-killers which can be produced by the body). (Lawrence1988). Acupressure is another type of massage which can be useful in the management of chronic pain. This is a finger massage to certain acupuncture points which works on the same principles as massage. If massage or acupressure is combined with pleasant smells, we have the techniques of aromatherapy which is becoming increasingly popular for the management of many conditions, including pain. Aromatherapy uses two of the senses; touch and smell.

Taste is a sense which is usually social. A meal is often enjoyed in the company of family or friends.

Certain foods can bring pleasure and can also bring back memories of times past. It is a basic human need to eat in order to survive, however, most people prefer to eat foods which they enjoy rather than those which are considered to be good for them. Taste also has a double meaning in that people can develop a "taste" for something like a certain type of music or clothes which can also bring them pleasure.

A great deal of pleasure can be derived from watching the sunset on a warm summers evening. Noting the red glow of the sky. The eyes are rather like a camera. They see images, focus on them and the images are recorded onto film which is the brain. At a later date, the images can be played back in the mind. Faces and places can be remembered in this way. Only in time, are these images forgotten but even then a certain smell or sound can send these images flooding back. These images can be of good or bad experiences. The eyes can behold beauty or they can see danger. Very often, pleasant images can be utilised when using relaxation techniques for pain management. If sight is lost, these images can still be played back in the mind. Also in the absence of sight, the other senses become more acute. We are surrounded by familiar sounds which are taken for granted. It is only when the clock stops ticking that it is noticed. Sounds can be manipulated to be soothing and therapeutic. The newborn baby is reassured by the sound of its mothers voice singing a lullaby. Even during development in the womb the sounds of the mother are reassuring, these sounds have been made available on tape for the nursery. Music is a powerful manipulation of sound. It can give rise to many emotions, a song which can make a person feel happy or sad, uplifting or calming emotions can be experienced.

The senses can protect people from pain, this has been demonstrated by the soldiers in the field of battle. They do not notice they have been injured. Their senses are so preoccupied with the sights and sounds all around them that the brain cannot cope with the additional sensation of pain. Saints and martyrs can also override the pain sensation by closing the pain gate with central control (the brain) thinking of the noble cause.

## The Snoezelen and Pain

The person with chronic pain wakes up every morning to the same sensation. Before they even open their eyes, notice the sounds around them or the smell of freshly brewed coffee, they become aware of the sensation of pain. This waking will probably have been preceded by a night of restless disturbed sleep, every movement interrupting their dreams with the constant reminder that the pain is still present. In some cases, the pain may even be worse due to the body becoming stiff with lying in the same position overnight. Individuals who are worried about a particular problem usually get a release from this worry during sleep although in the morning the problem floods back into the mind. The same happened to the person with chronic pain. On opening their eyes, the stressors and hassles related to the pain will return; the lost job or the loss of role within the family or society with subsequent financial worries.

These individuals will have also lost the ability to partake of their leisure pastimes or hobbies used by most as a form of relaxation to "unwind" from the everyday pressures of living. The pain will be present now for the rest of the day, a continuous reminder of the disability. Every menial task will be an enormous effort. Things which the person without pain would take for granted like peeling potatoes or answering the phone. The day becomes a mixture of boredom and excessive pain or exertion and finally at the end of the day another night of restless sleep.

Pain management programmes are designed to help to break the cycle and help people to live a reasonable quality of life with a degree of ongoing pain. The Snoezelen Facility is designed as "an opportunity for stimulation or relaxation with a development of relationships with carers" (Hutchinson 1992). This facility could enhance the conventional coping strategies taught on the pain management programme in Chesterfield.

## The Adventure Room

A large room containing softy shapes and a ball pool. This room, as its name suggests, could be an adventure for the individual with chronic pain. They can move around the room without risk or injury to themselves due to the soft floor. The ball pool would be ideal for these people, the body is totally supported without any pressure on painful joints. They can relax in the pool enjoying the feeling of being supported whilst listening to the soothing music and watching the coloured lights. The actual manoeuvre in and out of the pool will require encouragement and supervision, however, the experience is well worth the effort. All pain management programmes demand a certain amount of physical activity to improve joint mobility and strengthen wasted muscles. The experience in the adventure room can enable this exercise to be carried out in a more informal and relaxed way, the pleasure of the experience being the incentive. In the management of chronic pain, the adventure room would be facilitated by the pysiotherapist to ensure safety. The sensations within this area are touch, sight, sound and smell, combining to provide a mixture of activity and relaxation.

## The Jacuzzi Room

The present pain management programme provides people with access to the hydrotherapy pool. The warm water takes pressure off painful areas and allows more freedom of movement thus allowing gentle exercises to be carried out in the water. Individuals are encouraged to maintain this therapy themselves by attending the local swimming pool. At the end of a hard day most people find pleasure relaxing in a warm bath allowing tension to float away. Very often people with chronic pain comment on how helpful it is for them to soak in the bath, that is if they are able to get in. The jacuzzi is superb for these people for several reasons. First of all, access is relatively easy even for disabled people, there are no steps to negotiate and they can actually get in or out in the sitting position. The temperature of the water is reliably constant unlike that of the swimming pool. The therapeutic effect of the water is quite lost if the temperature of both the water and the surrounding atmosphere is not warm enough. If these temperatures are not right, the pain can actually be made worse. The jacuzzi has the advantage of water jets which can massage the body without any physical effort on the part of the patient, thus relieving tension in the muscle. The surroundings of the jacuzzi with its soft lighting, music and the bubble tube serve only to enhance the experience of relaxation whilst still proving a therapeutic experience. The jacuzzi experience can be maintained when the pain programme is completed as there are local facilities.

## The Sitting Room

This area, fitted with comfortable seating and with facilities for drinks, would be the ideal place for discussions. Information would be provided relating to the pain and methods of coping with advice on pacing activity, improving sleep and how to deal with pain flare-ups. Perhaps advice could also be given on setting up a suitable sensory environment at home to be used daily. This area is also far more relaxed than the present classroom situation which helps to break down the carer patient barriers essential when dealing with people in pain. A relationship of understanding, empathy and support must be developed which in turn leads to trust.

## The Sound and Light Room

An environment of light and sound technology which stimulates all of the senses, the room is easy to enjoy, even for the most disabled. The vibrating floor will be of particular interest in this room when used by people with pain, the effect will be monitored quite closely. There has been minimal research into the use of vibration in the management of pain (Loeser 1990).

## The White Room

Following the experiences of the previous rooms which involve physical effort, the white room provides the perfect environment for patients to relax and develop relaxation skills. The choice of comfortable furnishings, lights and soft music can enhance a relaxed state. The technique of relaxation was first conceived in the 1930's to reduce tension and anxiety. When psychologists began working with patients in pain relaxation became a key element of standard treatment. There is still a debate concerning mechanisms through which relaxation reduces pain, except in the relief of tension, for which there has been a consensus (Turner 1982). Various physiological changes have been reported which include the reduction of the heart rate and respiratory rate, increased skin resistance and changes in brain activity. Reduction in pain appears to be due to the relaxation of the muscles and reduced sympathetic activity. It has also been suggested that relaxation can cause changes in the level of Endorphins (morphine manufactured in the body). Relaxation is recommended where tension may be the cause of the pain or fear and tension may augment the pain problem. Much of the research on the effectiveness of relaxation in pain management has been carried out on patients with tension headaches (Turner J, Romano J 1984).

Even though relaxation is often used as one element of a set of cognitive behavioural treatments it has been demonstrated to reduce pain levels and medication as well as increasing functioning particularly successful in the treatment of low back pain. A study by Kabat and Sinn (1982) demonstrated that 2% of the patients were able to reduce their pain by 33% in addition to improvements in body image, activity, mood disturbance and medication intake.

The White Room facility provides the optimum setting for relaxation. The facilitator for this area would be the Clinical Psychologist who is skilled in the teaching of relaxation

222

techniques as applied to the patient with chronic pain. Usually the pain programme is carried out in a large classroom which is subject to background noise and interruptions. The far from clinical setting of the White Room will make the relaxation experience easier and more pleasurable, thus more effective. Patients could again continue to use the experience when the programme is complete by adopting some of the concepts from the White Room to apply in their own homes such as the soft lights, music and aromas.

Overall, the Snoezelen facility has tremendous potential for the running of pain management programmes with many advantages over the programmes currently organised within the hospital.

The main aim of the pain management programme is to teach people to live with a degree of ongoing pain and still have an acceptable quality of life. The Snoezelen facility moves totally away from the clinical hospital setting where investigations and treatments have been carried out, representing a definite move away from this form of management, relying on the acceptance of the pain as opposed to waiting for a cure.

The environment as it is not clinical, breaks down the care/patient barriers. This is particularly so due to the fact that the carers participate in the activities and share the experiences. This also happens with other group members which makes for better group cohesion.

Within the Snoezelen there is just the right mix of activity and relaxation. The activity is conducted without pressure unlike the conventional physical exercise in an interesting and innovative way. Therefore patients will be much more willing to participate. Leisure pastimes are usually carried out by individuals because they are enjoyable. The Snoezelen facility is also enjoyable thus making it a hobby but at the same time it can be therapeutic.

Chronic pain and stress are associated as discussed earlier. Therefore, the implications of the Snoezelen facility in the reduction of stress are a major factor to be considered in the management of pain. In the unlikely event that no other successful results can be obtained with this project, the stress reduction in itself will be a major accomplishment in the management of patients with chronic pain.

An environment which is a novelty to people will service to provide a distraction from the pain. Much research into the use of distraction techniques with pain has been carried out, particularly with the use of music therapy (Dalton 1987), Eland 1987, Fritz 1988). Chronic pain = lack of stimulation = boring and meaningless environment = focusing on the pain = decreased tolerance of pain. The Snoezelen facility breaks this cycle by providing stimulation in an interesting environment which also provides a distraction.

Distraction techniques are often used by parents of crying babies or children by demonstrating a toy or showing a rattle to distract the infant from a painful procedure. Many health care professionals use distraction techniques such as talking continuously during painful procedures to take the patients "mind off" the procedure. The Snoezelen facility expands this concept by bombarding all the senses simultaneously with sounds, smells, visions and textures providing the ultimate distraction experience.

Pain programmes conducted in the Snoezelen would be less structured and more informal than the conventional programmes allowing people freedom to explore the concepts at their own pace with active involvement and guidance from the carers. Moving away from the regime of being - "talked at" to one of group participation, thus facilitating self goal setting and pacing. When an individual develops chronic pain, often a strain develops within the family particularly with the spouse. It may be useful to encourage the spouse to participate in some of the sessions to redevelop a relationship of trust and understanding.

Assumptions can only be made at this stage regarding the success of running the pain management programme within an environment of sensory stimulation. However, there are clear advantages which point to the potential success of such an experiment.

1     The success of pain management programmes, both in America where they originated and in other countries has been widely documented. Using techniques for monitoring activity levels, medication intake and coping mechanisms. These assessments have been carried out both during and after participation in a programme and at follow up intervals to ensure that progress has been maintained. Ideally, the aim would be to assist individuals to return to work, however, in a climate of vast unemployment, this is an unrealistic expectation. Therefore to assist individuals to become more active, members of society would be a more realistic goal.

The Snoezelen facility at Whittington Hall Hospital is perfect for running this experiment, as the largest facility in the country, it could easily accommodate 12 individuals with chronic pain plus carers who could adapt the techniques used in conventional programmes to be applied in the far less intimidating environment of sensory stimulation.

2     Particular types of therapy which include relaxation techniques, distraction, physical therapy, massage, aromatherapy and music therapy have been reported to

be successful in the management of pain, either applied singularly or together in a structured programme.

These are examples of sensory input which can help the individual to focus less attention on his pain thus making the pain less intense and more tolerable.

3    Patients with chronic pain are exposed daily to an environment which is monotonous and boring. Because they cannot engage in the normal daily activities of living, they have a decreased sensory input. It has been suggested (Melzack, Stilwell and Fox 1977) that if a person is subjected to sufficient or excessive sensory stimulation, the pain mechanism can be blocked; closing the "pain gate". Examples of sensory input have been quoted previously. The Snoezelen concept is to provide a stimulating sensory environment if individuals are subjected to this environment sensory input will become excessive, thus the pain will be less focused on and consequently more tolerable. The normal healthy individual can obtain sensory input by listening to music or watching television, the person with chronic pain cannot usually concentrate on any of these things without the pain sensation "taking over". So, these normal levels of stimulation are not enough. Within the sensory environment the sensations are so powerful that techniques can be developed to enhance sensory stimulation which can be maintained at home for everyday use.

4    Actual enjoyment and fun which the Snoezelen proves can itself be therapeutic. Individuals with chronic pain have usually lost the ability to enjoy themselves to carry out activities simple for pleasure.

Most importantly, they can control their own environment thus participating in their care rather than having therapies "inflicted" upon them.

5    The use of the Snoezelen can make people feel 'special; saying to them "yes we believe you have a problem which is not straight forward and we recognise that you need help which is also not straight forward, but we can offer help which is unique".

## CONCLUSION

The Snoezelen certainly has potential with definite advantages over the conventional programmes within the clinical setting. The effectiveness of its application in the field of chronic pain requires careful monitoring before any definitely claim can be made. At this moment, it can only be said what could potentially happen. Therefore an organised research study is planned to assess the application in this field. The study will be conducted at the Whittington Hall Snoezelen facility in conjunction with the Chesterfield pain management service to assess the short and long term effects when used with people with chronic pain syndrome.

Success in the management of chronic pain could have major implications for many aspects of patient care. Within almost every setting patients are experiencing pain. It may be acute pain following trauma, surgery or in labour or pain associated with cancer. Snoezelen concepts could be applied in hospital wards or hospices. From very basic ideas on small scales to much large projects such as the White Room. The cost to the Health Service may not be great and is far outweighed by the potential savings. The potential reduction in medication and hospital treatment for patients could save the Health Service a large sum towards the 350 million pounds spent by the NHS on patients with chronic pain each year. This does not include the half billion pounds spent on DHSS benefits to back patients alone and the 3 billion pounds on lost production (Pither 1991). So, although sensory environments may cost initial capital, there is great scope for potential savings.

The Snoezelen is not just about saving the NHS money. There is also a major quality issue to be considered. If the Snoezelen was implemented in any care setting, patients would be more comfortable and therefore less anxious or depressed increasing patient satisfaction. Carers would feel less frustrated with the management of pain as the sensory environment could be used to enhance relaxation and distraction skills.

The Snoezelen experience at Whittington Hall cannot be underestimated or over emphasised. Its potential in the field of pain management can only be imagined!

**REFERENCES**

Arnoff G M and Evans W O. The prediction of treatment outcomes at a multidisciplinary pain centre. Pain 14 67-73 (1982).

Bond M R. Pain its nature analysis and treatment. Churchill Livingstone (1979).

Bonica J. The management of pain. Second edition. Lea and Febiger. Philadelphia, London (1990).

Crook J, Rideout E, Brown N E G. The prevalence of pain complaints in the general population. Pain 18 299 (1984).

Dalton J A. Education for pain management: A pilot study. Pat Educational Council 9 155-165 (1987).

Eland J. Personal Communication. University of Iowa (1987).

Eysenck H & Eysenck S G B. Manual of Eysenck personality inventory.
University of London (1964).

Fordyce W E. Behavioural methods in chronic pain and illness. CV Mosby. (1976)

Fritz D J. Non invasive pain control methods used by cancer outpatients.
Oncol. Nurs. Forum (1988).

Guck T P, Meilamn P W, Skultety F M. Pain assessment index: evaluation
multidisciplinary pain treatment. Arch Phys. Med. Rehab. 67 293-296 (1987).

Holmes T H & Rahe R H. The social readjustment rating scale.
J Psychosom Res 11 213-218 (1967).

Hutchinson R. Sensory Environments. North Derbyshire Health Authority (1992).
I.A.S.P. International association for the study of pain - sub committee on taxonomy
classification of chronic pain. Pain supplement 3 (1986).

Kabat Zinn J, Lipworth I, Burney R. The clinical use of mindfulness mediation for the self
regulation of chronic pain. J. Behav. Med*: 163 (1985).

Krieger D. The therapeutic touch, how to use your hands to help or heal.
New York: Prentice Hall (1979).

Lawrence L. Physiotheraphy in chronic pain from Chronic pain
by France R D & Krishman K R R. Amer psych. press (1988).

Loeser J. Pain after amputation. From the Management of Pain
by Bonica J, Lea and Febiger (1990).

Madjar I. Pain and the surgical patient, a cross cultural perspective.
Aus J Adv. Nurs 2: 29-33 (1985).

Meltzack R & Wall P. The puzzle of pain. Penguin Group London (1973).

Meltzack R, Stillwell DM, Fox EJ. Trigger Points and Acupuncture Points for pain
correlations and implications. Pain 3: 3-23 (1977).

Painter J R, Seres J I, Newman R I. Assessing the benefits of the pain centre: why some
patients regress. Pain 8: 101-113 (1980).

Pither C. Analysis of pain in the disabled social policy research unit. York University.
Unpublished report, information courtesy of Dr C Pither (1991).

Seyle H. The Stress of life. McGraw Hill. N.Y. (1956).

Sternback R A. Painn patients traits and treatments. New York Academic Press (1974).

Strelzer J, Wade T C. The influence of cultural group on the undertreatment of post-operative pain. Psychosomatic medicine 43 5: 397-403 (1981).

Taylor H. The Nuprin pain report. New York. Lou Harris & Associates (1985).

Turner J, Romano J. Evaluating Psychological interventions for chronic pain. New York Raven Press (1992).

Turner J, Chapman C. Psychological interventions for chronic pain: a critical view. Pain 12: 1-21 (1982).

Zborowski M. Cultural components in response to pain. Journal of social issues 8 4: 16-30 (1952)

# SENSORY ACTIVITY - A SUMMARY

**Roger Hutchinson**
**Joe Kewin**

We hope that the information provided in this book will stimulate the reader to consider the use of primary sensation in their everyday practice. When we first opened our Snoezelen centre at Whittington Hall in Chesterfield we had the idea that it would help our staff to provide experiences for people with a profound disability that were accessible and enjoyable. Since this beginning many different groups of people have visited or used our facilities. In the last twelve months sensory environments have been developed in Hospice Services and Neurological Rehabilitation. In Great Britain there are to date at least seventeen ongoing research projects evaluating the use of sensory activity with a wide variety of client populations.

Consideration is being given to the incorporation of Sensory ideas into the design of new facilities. In Chesterfield we are developing a new multi-million point specialist health care centre for people with severe disabilities. The sensory concept is being applied to both the external and internal inpatient, therapy and recreational environments. Concern for the quality of health care settings is causing architects and designers to incorporate sensory ideas into their new developments. Hopefully the time is rapidly approaching when 'clinical' or 'care' setting does not mean devoid of sensory stimulation. The time may well come when 'the patient' does not have to put up with care being delivered in a setting about as stimulating as a toilet. The environment itself can be designed to promote a sense of well being and control. Environments can be provided which allow the person with a sensory disability to access sensation that is meaningful to them.

A note of caution is necessary however. The environment itself can never compensate for inadequate, insensitive care delivered to the patient or client at 'arms length'. It is essential that staff working with people who are often confused or distressed take the time and trouble to develop a sensitive relationship that allows a meaningful dialogue between the provider and recipient of care. The 'right' environment, used in the 'right' way can greatly enhance the opportunities for dialogue to occur. The following summary of qualitative research findings clearly indicates the value of the sensory concept in developing this dialogue.

## Whittington Hall Project:

*    Self Injurious Behaviour did not happen in Snoezelen
   *    The environment was not damaged

* Staff/client interactions improved
* Generalisation of effects occurred
* Clients made choices
* Clients relaxed
* Clients enjoyed the experiences

## Haggar Training Package:

* High frequencies of client/care interaction
* High frequencies of socialisation behaviour
* Low rates of rejection in Snoezelen
* Staff can learn new skills

## Limington House Project:

* Snoezelen is a valuable leisure resource
* Snoezelen aids positive programming
* There is an increase in the repertoire of skills
* The repair or damaged relationships is facilitated
* A possible reduction in challenging behaviour

## King Park Community Units:

* Of value in developing therapeutic relationships
* Snoezelen provides quality time
* Trust, sharing and equality develop
* Snoezelen activity is failure free
* Staff find it rewarding
* Carers can achieve
* Feelings of uselessness can be avoided

## Dana Henning:

* Able to prevent some self injury
* Allows space to be shared
* Restraints/helmets can be removed
* Snoezelen can be incorporated into a treatment plan
* The identification of objectives is facilitated

It appears that an activity which was initially seen as an alternative to traditional practice is rapidly becoming a 'mainstream' provision. The extent to which this may happen is dependent upon the degree to which you, the reader, use your creative skills in the application of primary sensory experience with your service users.

# SENSATIONS AND DISABILITY

## AUTHORS

**IERVYN BALSON**
eadmaster at Limington House School for Children with Special Needs, Basingstoke, England. Mervyn has also worked in pecial Education in the United States.

**'AUL BARKER**
'sychologist at Kings Park Community Hospital, Bournemouth, England.

**A. BUNSEN**
Deputy Head Teacher at Limington House School for Children with Special Needs, Basingstoke, England.

**M. GALLAHER**
Teacher at Limington House School for children with Special Needs, Basingstoke, England.

**LOUISE HAGGAR**
Clinical Psychologist in North Derbyshire Learning Disability Services, England.

**JILL HARRIS**
Occupational Therapy Manager in North Derbyshire Learning Disability Services, England.

**DANA HENNING**
Doctor of Education at Dana Henning Training Programmes, Langhorne, Pa, USA.

**ROGER HUTCHINSON**
Consultant Clinical Psychologist and Manager of Clinical Support Services in North Derbyshire Learning Disability Services, England.

**JOE KEWIN**
Formerly District Occupational Therapist, now General Manager of North Derbyshire Learning Disability Services, England, and the person who initiated the SNOEZELEN concept in Great Britain.

**PAULINE McALLISTER**
Nurse, Mental Health Unit at Chesterfield & North Derbyshire Royal Hospital NHS Trust, England.

**MARIANNE MELLBERG & GUNILLA JANSSON**
Joint Head Teachers at a school for children with special needs at Traningsskolan Baldershus in Norrtalje, Sweden.

**ANITA MOORE**
Physiotherapy Manager in North Derbyshire Learning Disability Services, England.

**LESLEY PINKNEY**
Lecturer in Occupational Therapy at Wessex School of Occupational and Physiotherapy, faculty of Southampton University.

**PAT SCHOFIELD**
Senior Nurse Specialist in charge of the Chronic Pain Clinic at Chesterfield & N. Derbyshire Royal Hospital NHS Trust, England.

**KATE SMITH**
Occupational Therapist, Mental Health Unit at Chesterfield & North Derbyshire Royal Hospital NHS Trust, England.

**JUDY STEPHENS**
Speech & Language Therapy Manager in North Derbyshire Learning Disability Services, England.